CLOZE STORIES FOR READING SUCCESS

Helen Shangold

Walker Educational Book Corporation

720 Fifth Avenue, New York, N.Y. 10019

Design: RFS Graphic Design, Inc.

Cover Design: Marsha Picker

This edition published in 1991

First published in the United States of America in 1981 by the Walker Publishing Company, Inc.

ISBN: 0-8027-9124-7

Printed in the United States of America
10 9 8 7 6 5

Introduction

Cloze Stories for Reading Success is a series of 122 student worksheets designed to reinforce basic decoding and to enhance reading comprehension. A total of approximately 1200 words are presented in the lessons.

The worksheets employ the "cloze technique," which requires the student to supply (close) missing key words using clues provided in the reading passage. In some cases, closure may be automatic for the child; the word to be filled in will be the obvious choice. In other cases, the student may need to apply one or several clues in order to select the appropriate word. Clues may be provided by the context of the story, or the word may be suggested by punctuation, capitalization, the order of the word in the sentence, the tense of a verb or number of a noun, or the descriptive adjectives or adverbs preceding the missing word.

The *Cloze Stories* are organized in the alphabetical sequence used by Philip J. McInnis in the Primary Level of the *Decoding Keys for Reading Success.** The Decoding Key emphasized in the lesson appears at the top of each page. However, the stories are compatible, with almost all contemporary reading programs including the most widely used basal reading series.

Skill Areas. The *Cloze Stories for Reading Success* develop a number of essential language arts skills. The ability to spot clues and apply them has wide application for reading comprehension at all levels. In addition, these stories provide review and reinforcement in the reading, writing, and spelling of over 1200 common words. In discovering answers for the *Cloze Stories*, the student is rewarded for recognizing the word and knowing its meaning. Consequently, these words become a part of the student's functional reading and speaking vocabulary.

Teaching Suggestions. If the instructor is using the Decoding Keys Program, it is suggested that a worksheet be presented two or three days after the review of the appropriate Decoding Key. Ideally, these stories should be used as the final activity devoted towards the assured mastery of each Decoding Key.

If the teacher is not using the Decoding Keys, he or she may select the *Cloze Story* that complements the reading lesson on which the student is currently working by referring to the Decoding Key listed at the top of each lesson.

Cloze Stories for Reading Success may be used for one-to-one, small-group, or classroom instruction.

The recommended procedure for using *Cloze Stories* in one-to-one situations is for the student first to read the story silently, making no effort to complete the blanks. Then he or she should read aloud the accompanying Word List, which is included immediately below the reading passage. The instructor should ask if the child understands the meaning of each word; if not, the teacher should define the unfamiliar words.

---

*Philip J. McInnis. *Decoding Keys for Reading Success*. New York: Walker Educational Book Corporation, 1981.

Next, the student should read the entire story aloud, select the correct word from the Word List as he goes along, and write the appropriate word in each blank. If the child has difficulty choosing a word, the instructor may point to clues in nearby words or phrases that may aid the student in finding the answer. Trial-and-error may also be used; the student may try different words in the list to see if they "make sense."

It is often helpful if the student places a check mark in front of each word in the Word List as it is used. Since each word is used only once, the choice becomes narrowed down as the child reads through the story. Do not let the student cross out the word; if an error is made, it will be more difficult to spot.

If the student makes a mistake, be sure that he or she understands why the choice was incorrect and why the correct word is the proper choice. When all blanks have been filled in, ask the student to read the completed story aloud.

In a small group or classroom, the procedure is basically the same. However, the students should work silently and independently as they fill in the blank spaces. In the final step, the reading of the completed story, the instructor should allow the students to take turns reading a section of the story aloud. Students should be encouraged to discuss which clues aided them in their word choices.

A few days after the student has successfully completed a cloze story, the instructor may wish to follow up the activity with the corresponding crossword puzzle in *Crosswords for Reading Success*. The *Crosswords* review key words in the *Cloze Stories* and provide further reading, writing, and spelling practice.

NAME ______________________ DATE ______________

ABBY'S PET

Abby was a city girl who loved animals. She liked to go to the zoo to see the ______________. She had a ______________ of going there on her way home from school. When she crossed the street she had to be careful not to be hit by the ______________ as they raced by. She wished she could live in a ______________ in the woods. She'd have a garden and grow ______________ to feed the bunny ______________.

One day when Abby's father came home from the ______________ where he worked he had a surprise for her. It was a ______________ kitten. She had wanted a rabbit, but she knew a tabby kitten was a better pet in an apartment.

WORD LIST

Choose the missing word to complete each sentence.

lab	habit	baboon
cabs	tabby	cabbage
cabin	rabbits	

NAME ______________________ **DATE** ______________

FEELING BETTER

Mable had had a cold for two days. She felt stuffy and __________. She stayed in bed and was __________ to go to school. She listened to the radio. Her mother read her favorite __________ from her book called *Aesop's Fables*. On the third afternoon she was __________ to get up. She sat at the dining room __________ and cut out pictures for her scrap book. She found a picture of horses running in a field with their __________ in the background. There was a picture of a spooky old house with a __________ at each end of its roof line. The picture she liked best was a scene in San Francisco that showed a __________ climbing a hill, with the bay and bridge in the distance. When her mother told her it was time to set the table for dinner, she put her things away. She helped her mother spread the __________. Then Mable set the table, being very careful for she knew that the china and glasses were __________. Mable felt so much better. She was sure she would go back to school tomorrow.

WORD LIST

Choose the missing word to complete each sentence.

able	breakable	cablecar
fable	stables	miserable
gable	tablecloth	
table	unable	

NAME ______________________ DATE ______________

A CAREER PROJECT

Miss MacRae had a career project in her class. She asked the children to think about what they would like to do when they were grown-ups. She asked them to make a list of every ______________ they could think of about themselves. She told them to include the things they had been __________ in and to consider each ______________ to see if it might suggest a career. She asked them to think about what made that career ______________ to them. Here are a few of the choices the children made:

Jan said that ever since her parents had taken her to see "Peter Pan" she had wanted to be an ______________.

Pete reported that he loved taking care of plants and that his __________ collection was his main interest. He wants to own a plant nursery.

Jim said that ever since he had been in a class play in third grade he had loved ______________. When he grows up he wants to be an __________.

Tim said that he had been taken to the hospital when he had an __________ on his bike. He wants to be a doctor.

Ann told about her pet ______________, which she has raised since it was a baby. She wants to be a veterinarian.

Lee likes machines and likes to figure out how they work. He wants to be a foreman in a ______________.

Sue likes to ______________ for her music lessons. She thinks she would like to be a music teacher.

Have you thought about what you would like to be when you grow up?

WORD LIST

Choose the missing word to complete each sentence.

fact	cactus	practice
acting	actress	activity
active	accident	factory
actor	raccoon	attractive

NAME ________________________________ DATE ________________

LATE GRACE

There was a girl named ______________ who took such a long time to get ready for school that she was always late. It took her a long time to brush her teeth because she wore ______________. She was always careful to ______________ the cap on the toothpaste, but it took time. She was slow when she washed her ______________ too. When she got dressed, first she ______________ her shoes, then she had to ________ them back up again. Sometimes she would just sit and look off into ______________. She had a ______________ on the hall table to put her books and homework, but sometimes she would ______________ them. Then she had to spend time looking for them. She always gave her mother a quick kiss and an ______________. Then off she would ________ to school.

WORD LIST

Choose the missing word to complete each sentence.

face	Grace	replace
lace	space	misplace
race	braces	unlaced
place	embrace	

NAME ______________________________ DATE ________________

JACK'S SUMMER

There was a boy named ______________ who lived in the city. Every summer he went to visit his grandfather and grandmother on their farm. His mother packed his things and gave him a gift ______________ to take with him. She took him to the train and waited near the ______________ until he left. When he got to the farm, he liked to play with his grandma's ______________ cat. The place he liked best was the ______________. He took ______________ to eat. He sat on his ______________ and listened to the ______________ of the hens and the ______________ of the ducks. What a ______________ they made! When his grandma called, he went ______________ into the house to help her ______________ nuts for a cake. Life on a farm seems good to a city boy.

WORD LIST

Choose the missing word to complete each sentence.

back	black	backside
Jack	cackle	crackers
track	quack	racket
crack	haystack	package

NAME ______________________________ DATE ______________

ADAM'S SAD DAY

A boy named ______________ sat on the bank of a pond. He saw the ______________ of a tree in the water. Now and then a __________ swam by. He felt like crying, he was so ______________. He knew that when his ______________ came home he'd have to ________ that he had broken the window. It ______________ happened when the ______________ hit against it. He wished he ______________ tried to climb in the window. He took the money from his pocket to __________ it up again. It was not enought to pay for the glass. Adam started to walk home. "I will be ______________ after I have told __________," he said to himself.

WORD LIST

Choose the missing word to complete each sentence.

had	glad	hadn't
dad	admit	Daddy
add	Adam	shadow
sad	tadpole	ladder

NAME ______________________________ DATE ________________

THE LAST DAY OF SCHOOL

On the last day of school before vacation the first and second __________ in the school had a picnic. They marched in a ______________ to the park. There they found a spot ________________ by trees for their picnic. They drank ________________ and ate sandwiches. They loved the cookies with orange ________________ filling. Some of the children took off their socks and shoes so they could ________________ in the pool. Other children sat in the sandbox and ________________ sand castles or dug holes with a small ________________. Other children followed a grasshopper as it jumped from one ________________ of grass to another. Then it was time to return to school. They all had a wonderful time.

WORD LIST

Choose the missing word to complete each sentence.

made	spade	lemonade
wade	shaded	marmalade
blade	grades	parade

NAME ____________________ DATE ____________

DAYDREAMS

It was late on a warm ____________ in May. Don sat on the front steps and chewed a piece of sweet, sticky ____________. He watched the ____________ as it passed in the street. He saw a pot of pretty, yellow ____________ in a window across the street. He felt a ____________ of warm air smelling of exhaust fumes as a bus passed by. He longed for the summer ____________ school had closed. How he wished he could be somewhere else.

He closed his eyes and wondered what it would be like to float down a river on a ____________. Perhaps he could win a ____________ and have enough money to go far away to ____________. He would wear a ____________ like the natives and walk through the market place buying the local hand ____________.

Then his mother and father came out and said that they were all going to the ____________ around the corner for dinner. That was as far as Don went that warm day in May.

WORD LIST

Choose the missing word to complete each sentence.

raft	after	cafeteria
draft	traffic	caftan
taffy	afternoon	raffle
crafts	daffodils	Africa

NAME ______________________________ DATE ________________

MAGGIE GOES SHOPPING

Maggie went shopping for a gift for her brother. She looked in her hand ________________ to see how much money she had to spend. First she looked at a red ________________ with four big wheels. When she looked at the price ________________ she went on. Perhaps he'd like a ________ to play a tune, or a ________________ to pick up pins and tacks, or a rubber ________________ to put in his belt when he played pirate. She saw a red, white, and blue ________________ that would fit on his tricycle. Then she went to the pet store and saw a puppy that ________________ his tail when he looked at her. Which of these do you think Maggie will buy?

WORD LIST

Choose the missing word to complete each sentence.

bag	dagger	magnet
tag	wagged	bagpipe
flag	wagon	

NAME ______________________________ DATE ________________

STORIES OF THE OLD WEST

John turned the last ____________ of the book. He hated to see it end. On the book's ____________ he had read the story of western travel. It was a time when the ____________ still followed the rocky trails through the ____________. He had read of the ____________ of the cowboys as the farmers settled the land. He had read about a government ____________ who had been sent to ____________ a battle against the outlaws. There was a story about a farmer who kept rattlesnakes ____________ in a strong wire ____________ in his backyard. He liked the story of an ____________ prospector who grew older and older as he spent his years searching for gold in California. These stories all happened long ago, but John felt American pioneer life had an ____________ appeal, at least it did for him.

WORD LIST

Choose the missing word to complete each sentence.

page	agent	ageless
cage	aged	stagecoach
wage	caged	sagebrush
rage	pages	

NAME ______________________ DATE ____________

WAITING FOR THE TRAIN

The railroad station was a small, ____________ building. Jane and her mother went inside, and her mother ____________ for their tickets. She said to Jane, "We will have to ____________ fifteen minutes until our ____________ comes."

Jane didn't want to ____________, but she felt a bit ____________ to ride on the train. She didn't know if she could ____________ it to her mother. They went out on the platform to wait. Jane looked down the tracks. They were so ____________ as they went off into the distance. Then she looked up at the sky and wondered if it were going to ____________. Of course, once they were on the train it would not matter to them if it did rain. Then Jane said to herself, "If I would just use my ____________, I would know that there is no reason to be afraid."

WORD LIST

Choose the missing word to complete each sentence.

wait	plain	complain
train	afraid	straight
rain	brains	
paid	explain	

NAME ______________________ DATE ______________

A NEW SAILBOAT

Alan likes any kind of toy that moves. He has cars, trucks, and a ______________ set. He didn't have any toy that moved in water until yesterday when his father brought him a ______________. Alan decided to take his sailboat to the park so he could ______________ it there. He asked his dog, Rover, if he wanted to go, and Rover wagged his ________. On the way to the park they passed the ______________ carrying his large bag of mail. Alan saw a lady ______________ a letter in the mail box outside the post office. When he got to the park he saw children playing in the sand box with their shovels and ______________. Alan and Rover walked along the ______________ to the pond. When they got to the pond, he set his sailboat in the water. He and Rover watched as it went ______________ across the water. Alan knew that he would be enjoying this gift for a long time.

WORD LIST

Choose the missing word to complete each sentence.

tail	pails	railroad
trail	mailman	mailing
sail	sailing	sailboat

NAME ______________________ DATE ______________

A TRIP TO THE AIRPORT

Patty's grandmother was ready to return home after her visit. Patty and her mother took her to the ______________. They found the ticket window for the ______________ her grandmother was going on. She checked in and left her luggage. Then they went up the ______________ to the waiting room ______________. Her mother and grandmother found ______________ and sat down. Patty went to the window where she could look out and see all the ______________ down below. She could see a plane being moved to a hanger for ______________ before its next flight. When it was time for her grandmother to board her ______________, Patty said, "I think it is ______________ for you to leave us so soon." After she and her mother kissed her grandmother good-by, they went down the ______________ and out to their car.

Her mother said, "Patty, next vacation you can go visit Grandma. I'm sure she will take you to the ______________ by her home and you will see how cream is made."

WORD LIST

Choose the missing word to complete each sentence.

stairs	dairy	stairway
chairs	unfair	airplane
airline	airport	upstairs
aircraft	repair	

NAME ______________________ DATE ______________

A FALL JOB

As soon as Tom was ____________ on Saturday morning he remembered what he had to do. It was Tom's job to ____________ the leaves when they fell in the fall. His mother said it was important to rake them all before the first ____________ fell from the clouds in winter. When he finished she said that she would ____________ him to the ____________ for a treat. She would let him ____________ a choice of the ____________ he wanted. When they returned home they made a ____________ for him to drink while he ate his ____________.

WORD LIST

Choose the missing word to complete each sentence.

make	rake	bakery
take	cakes	milkshake
cake	awake	snowflake

NAME ______________________ DATE ______________

SUMMER DREAMS

On a rainy Saturday morning ______________ looked at the ______________ on her mother's desk. She saw that there were only four more weeks of school. She turned to her brother, ______________, and asked, "What ______________ we do all summer long?"

Alan replied, "If I could do anything I wanted, I would live on a ranch in a western ______________ with the hills all around. I would work in the ______________ with the cowboys. Maybe my ______________, Bill, could come ______________."

Sally said, "That wouldn't suit me at all. I would like to live in a ______________ in Venice that overlooked a ______________."

Just then their mother called them. She said, "Come have your lunch. The tuna ______________ is ready." They put their summer dreams aside for awhile as they went to have lunch.

WORD LIST

Choose the missing word to complete each sentence.

pal	shall	valley
also	canal	corral
Sally	salad	calendar
Alan	palace	

NAME ______________________________ DATE ________________

A GRANDFATHER'S TALES

Gale always looked forward to her grandfather's visits. He had many ____________ to tell of the time long ago when he was a sailor. He told Gale of seeing the great, gray ____________ swimming in the Pacific Ocean. He remembered the song of the ____________ in the French countryside when he was on shore leave. He once saw ____________ of cotton waiting to be shipped from the dock in New Orleans after being weighed on the ____________. He watched as ____________ dolphins gathered to protect the new-born offspring of a mother dolphin. He even had a ____________ to tell of the time he saw a ____________ walrus fight to protect his territory from the younger males. He stood watch many a night and saw the ____________ moon fade in the sky as the sun rose in the east. He'd like to be able to ____________ that good sea air just one more time. But for now he is happy to tell his tales to Gale.

WORD LIST

Choose the missing word to complete each sentence.

tale	tales	female
pale	whale	nightingale
male	inhale	
bales	scales	

NAME ______________________ DATE ______________

A SATURDAY MORNING BALL GAME

One Saturday morning a boy named ____________ went out the door of his apartment into the ____________ of the building. He held a ____________ in his hand. He tossed the ball into the air and caught it as it was ____________. He was careful that it didn't hit the ________ on the walls because he knew that it would leave marks. As he walked over to the playground he ____________ to his friends who were already there.

"Where are ____________ the other boys?" he asked Jim, who was the ____________ boy there.

Jim answered, "Well, you know Dan and Tim are ____________ late. We could ask Tommy to play, but he is too ____________ to be playing with us."

Walter replied, "We were supposed to play at ten o'clock. I don't like this ____________ around. Let's go ____________ Dan and Tim. Tommy can play ____________. We can use him."

Just as he went to make the call, he saw Dan and Tim coming around the corner. Then they were able to start the game.

WORD LIST

Choose the missing word to complete each sentence.

all	Walter	called
also	stalling	always
ball	tallest	wallpaper
call	falling	
small	hallway	

NAME ______________________ DATE ______________

A FAMILY CAMPING TRIP

During the long winter ____________ liked to think about the summer when she and her ____________ took a camping trip. They liked to ____________ out in the woods. They set their tent under a pine tree near a ____________. In the mornings they went for a long ____________ through the woods. Pam had to ____________ her hair in the stream near the dam. For dinner they cooked ____________ or ____________ over a campfire. At night they had an oil ________ for light. She was glad that her pet ____________ was so small that she could bring him in his cage on the trip.

WORD LIST

Choose the missing word to complete each sentence.

Pam	lamp	hamburger
dam	tramp	hamster
ham	shampoo	
camp	family	

NAME ______________________ DATE ____________

A RACCOON NAMED HALLOWEEN

Last Halloween James' father ____________ home from hunting with a baby raccoon. When he first got the raccoon it was wild and ________. James put him in a cage and started to think of a ________ to call him. He ____________ him Halloween because he got him on Halloween. Also, James thought that a raccoon looks as if he is wearing a mask. Later he shortened the raccoon's name and gave him the __________ of Hal. After a few months of good care and plenty of food Hal __________ used to his new life. James felt he was now ____________. They even had a ____________ they played together. James hid peanuts in his pockets and Hal looked for them. They played the ________ game over and over, and Hal never tired of it.

WORD LIST

Choose the missing word to complete each sentence.

came	game	untamed
name	tame	became
same	named	nickname

NAME ______________________ DATE ______________

ANN WRITES TO SANTA

Christmas was coming. It was time for ____________ to write her letter to ____________ Claus. She sat down and ____________ to think. She took a ____________ to eat while she was thinking. She loved music and asked for a ____________ to play. She liked to ____________ and needed a new pair of tap shoes. She loved ____________ such as her kitten and puppy. She wanted to ask for ____________ pet. "I'd rather have a bunny rabbit ____________ a hamster," she said to herself. "I want a ____________ to put on my window sill, too. I ____________ think of anything else I want. Santa Claus is a good ____________. I hope he will not think I have asked for too much."

WORD LIST

Choose the missing word to complete each sentence.

man	began	banana
than	dance	Santa
Ann	cannot	animals
plant	banjo	another

NAME ______________________________ DATE ______________

A DAY WITH GRANDPA

There was a boy named ____________ who always liked the days he spent with his ____________. Andy met him on the stair ____________ so his grandfather would not have to climb the steps. Andy always held grandpa's ____________ when they crossed the street. Sometimes they went to the park so Andy could play in the ________, or they went to the zoo to see the ____________. The best times were when there was a parade. They could ____________ at the curb and listen to the ____________ play. For lunch they ate a ________ and then a ____________ bar. When they got home Andy always said, "I had a ____________ time," ____________ Grandpa always said, "I had a grand time too."

WORD LIST

Choose the missing word to complete each sentence.

and	stand	sandwich
hand	Andy	landing
band	panda	grandfather
grand	candy	sandbox

NAME ______________________ DATE ______________

A SUMMER VISIT

Last summer ____________ and her mother flew south to visit her grandmother and grandfather. Jane liked the trip on the ____________. As soon as the ____________ landed Jane looked over the crowd until she saw her grandfather, leaning on his ____________. Her grandmother was at his side. As they left the airport Jane saw that there was a lot of building going on along the road. When they stopped for a red light she watched as a ____________ lifted a heavy beam. After a short drive they turned off the highway onto the ____________ that led to her grandfather's farm. When they got to the farm Jane ran to the meadow to see Star, her grandfather's horse. She gave Star a lump of sugar and ran her hand through the shiny hair of her ____________. When she went into the house she saw that her grandmother had the long stalks of sweet, juicy ____________ waiting for her. As she sat chewing on the sugarcane she looked out the ____________ at her grandmother's garden.

When two weeks had passed it was time to go back to the city. Her grandparents thought Jane and her mother were ____________ to leave the farm for the city. Jane promised to come back next year as she and her mother boarded the plane.

WORD LIST

Choose the missing word to complete each sentence.

cane	mane	windowpane
Jane	plane	sugarcane
lane	insane	
crane	airplane	

NAME ______________________________ DATE ______________

THE OLD WEST ON TELEVISION

The television programs that Jim likes best are about the old west. He has heard the ______________ of the first train as it crossed the plains. He has seen a ______________ of outlaws rob the train. He has watched the hero tame a wild ______________. He has held his breath as the hero saved a child when a rattlesnake was about to sink its __________ into him. He has cheered as an ______________ crowd saved the hero when the bad men were about to ______________ him. He has heard the ______________ of guns in many thrilling escapes. One cowboy even ______________ to his horse as he played his guitar and rode off into the sunset. Sometimes Jim thinks he would like to live just like a cowboy.

WORD LIST

Choose the missing word to complete each sentence.

bang	sang	angry
hang	fangs	mustang
gang	clanging	

NAME ______________________ DATE ______________

A FRIENDLY RANGER

When Steve and his family went camping in a state park last summer he got to know the ____________ who worked there. At first Steve did not talk to him because he was a ____________. After a day or two Steve became friendlier with him. Steve wanted to know if the work was ever ____________. The ranger told him that if you know what kind of ____________ to expect you can learn to handle it. Steve's parents thought that it was ____________ that Steve should follow the ranger around. Steve helped him ____________ the nature exhibits. The ranger pointed out to Steve the ____________ that were taking place in nature with the approach of fall. The ____________ thing the ranger told him was that any snakes that lived in the park were not to be killed, as they were part of the balance of nature. The day before they had to leave Steve was sad. His parents thought that he spoke ____________ when he told the ranger goodbye. Then they told him they would be coming back next year. He felt better and went to tell the ranger.

WORD LIST

Choose the missing word to complete each sentence.

danger	arrange	stranger
ranger	changes	strangest
strange	strangely	dangerous

NAME ______________________ DATE ______________

GIVING THANKS

Before the Banks family ate their turkey on ____________ Day they gave ____________ for all the good things they had. After dinner Mr. Banks asked everyone to tell one thing they were thankful for. While the grown-ups ____________ their coffee, this is what they talked about.

Uncle ____________ said he was thankful that he had a full ____________ of gas in his car.

Little Ted was thankful that he had money in his piggy ____________ so he could buy Christmas presents.

Tom was thankful that his ____________ had healed so that he could play football again.

Jim was thankful that his mother didn't ____________ him for taking a piece of pumpkin pie before dinner.

Aunt Sue was thankful that Baby Timmy was not cross and ________ any longer.

Jan was thankful for the pretty, new, warm ____________ on her bed.

What are you thankful for?

WORD LIST

Choose the missing word to complete each sentence.

tank	ankle	cranky
bank	Frank	Thanksgiving
drank	spank	
thanks	blanket	

NAME ______________________ DATE ______________

BILLY'S NAP

Billy sat on the step eating an __________. He wanted something to do. He wished something would __________. Then his mother called and said it was time for a __________. He did not like naps, but he lay down and closed his eyes. Soon he was walking __________ through the jungle with a hunter's __________ on his head. He was a __________ catching animals for a zoo. He set a __________ with __________ of food. He hid until he heard the trap __________ closed. How __________ he was to catch his first animal! Then he heard the sound again. It was Tim rapping on his door. His nap was over. He and Tim could go out to play.

WORD LIST

Choose the missing word to complete each sentence.

cap	happy	trapper
nap	apple	happen
snap	scraps	
trap	rapidly	

NAME ______________________ DATE ______________

ANN'S ART CLASS

The class Ann likes best is art. One day she took a sheet of ________ and cut colored paper into many ____________. She glued them to her paper to make a collage. Before Halloween she painted a witch in a long, black ____________. Once after a class trip to the zoo she drew a picture of an ____________ in his cage. He was shaking the bars trying to ____________. She has painted a big bowl of fruit with a round, yellow ____________, red apples, and a bunch of purple ________. Her teacher puts the best work on the display board in the hall with scotch ____________. Ann is so proud when one of her pictures is put on the board.

WORD LIST

Choose the missing word to complete each sentence.

ape	shapes	escape
paper	grapes	grapefruit
cape	tape	

NAME ________________________________ DATE ________________

SUMMER ON A FARM

Last summer ______________ left his home in the city to go __________ away. He went to stay with a ______________ and his family. The farmer met the bus, and they rode to the farm in his ______. The farmer's son, Hank, took Charles by the ______________, and they went out to look around the ______________. After dinner they sat on the porch until it got ______________ and the first __________ appeared in the sky. Then they made a fire and toasted __________. On Fridays Charles went with Hank and his family to the farmers' ______________ where they sold their vegetables. Charles had such a good time that the weeks soon passed. It seemed he had __________ started his visit, when it was time to go home. On the last day of his visit Charles was given a farewell ______________. Then it was time to __________ home.

WORD LIST

Choose the missing word to complete each sentence.

far	arm	market
car	dark	Charles
farmer	star	marshmallows
party	hardly	
start	barnyard	

NAME ______________________ DATE ______________

A BELGIAN HARE

Mary loved animals. Of all her pets, the one she liked best was a Belgian ______________. This hare was not like the rabbits that were common where she lived. In fact, it was quite ______________. She took very good ______________ of him. He had a large ______________ cage with wire sides. Mary knew that she had to ______________ of the dogs by her house. Sometimes they ran through her back yard if the gate in the fence was left open. If they got in the dogs would ______________ at the hare through the wire and growl. Mary could see that the hare had reason to be ______________. She tried to be ______________ when the dogs were running loose in the ______________. She was ______________ to see that the gate was kept closed. That way they couldn't get into the back yard, and her pet was safe.

WORD LIST

Choose the missing word to complete each sentence.

care	aware	stare
rare	square	beware
hare	careful	
area	scared	

NAME ______________________________ DATE ____________________

BOBBY'S CAR

Bobby made a car out of a soap box and four wheels. It was red and yellow and very ______________. Instead of a head light he had a ______________. It was on the ______________ of the car. One day he was ______________ down a hill and did not look where he was going. He ______________ into a tree. Oh what a ______________-up that was! But at least he saved the wheels. He put the broken soap box and flashlight in the ______________. Then he counted his ______________ to see if he had the money he needed to buy a new flashlight.

WORD LIST

Choose the missing word to complete each sentence.

cash	flashy	flashlight
smash	dashing	dashboard
trash	crashed	

NAME ______________________________ DATE ______________

JACK'S NEW GLASSES

This was the first morning that Jack was wearing ____________ to school. He could see better when he was wearing them, but just thinking about walking into his fourth grade ____________ worried him. Everyone would be ____________ why he was wearing glasses. How could anyone be so silly as to ____________ a question like that?

As he went out the front door his dog, ____________, joined him. She seemed to know how he was feeling. He turned back as he closed the door to look at his reflection in the shiny plate of the ____________ door knocker. Then he and Lassie walked across the ____________ of the front lawn. As he was ____________ along the street he came to a trash ____________. For just a moment he thought it would be great if he could put his glasses in it; but he decided to ____________ on. As he came to the corner he could smell the odor of ____________ from the service station. Then he saw his friend, Fred. Fred said, "Hi, Jack. I see you have your new glasses. They are really neat. Did you finish all your math problems?" The two friends walked on to school as if nothing were different.

WORD LIST

Choose the missing word to complete each sentence.

pass	glasses	basket
ask	grass	Lassie
class	passing	gasoline
brass	asking	

NAME ______________________________ DATE ______________

FAST TRAVEL

Don Pastor has always been fond of anything that could go fast. Once he rode so ______________ on his bike that he had an accident. He went ______________ a red light and ran into a car. He had to be taken to the hospital to have a ______________ put on his leg. That was the ________ time he rode that fast on his bike. Then he began to collect model planes and rockets. The plane he likes best is the SST, which can go ______________ than any other plane in his collection. The __________ way of all to travel is by rocket ship. When Don grows up he hopes that he can be an ______________. He has watched the rockets ________ off on TV. Every time he sees one ______________ off he wishes that he could ______________ the future so he could be sure that he would be in a rocket some day. For now, he saves his money and buys ______________ models of the planes and rockets he dreams of flying.

WORD LIST

Choose the missing word to complete each sentence.

fast	blast	fastest
cast	faster	forecast
last	blasting	astronaut
past	plastic	

NAME ______________________ DATE ______________

TABBY, THE CAT

It was a warm ______________ afternoon. Tabby, the ________, used her paws to ______________ the bark of a tree. A ___________ of bark fell off. Then she went and ______________ in the sun to watch for the ______________ that lived under the wooden _________. ______________ rat had been getting ______________ and fatter, but he still ran fast. Tabby could not catch him. She could hear him scratch the wood of the platform, but he did not come out. For all I can tell, Tabby may still be sitting there ______________ that platform.

WORD LIST

Choose the missing word to complete each sentence.

at	That	platform
rat	patch	Saturday
sat	fatter	
cat	scratch	

NAME ______________________________ DATE ______________

KATE GOES SKATING

It was getting ______________. ______________ sat at the table looking at her ______________. There was still half of a sandwich on it. Her mother had said that she could not go out to skate until she ________ all of her lunch. She was ______________ that her mother took such good care of her, but she wished that she could eat the sandwich ______________. She had a ______________ to go skating with Ann. She stuffed the sandwich in her mouth and went to get her jacket and skates. As she went out the door she saw her ______________ was waiting for her at the ______________. She went through the ______________, and the two girls went to the pond to join the other ______________.

WORD LIST

Choose the missing word to complete each sentence.

ate	late	skaters
date	plate	playmate
gate	later	gateway
Kate	grateful	

NAME ______________________ DATE ______________

A BUSY SUMMER

It was the middle of ______________. The summer vacation was almost over. Audrey had helped her mother as much as she could. She often started fixing dinner ______________ she knew her mother was ______________ when she came home from work. She always used great ______________ when using the gas stove. She helped keep her little brother busy with games and saw that he did not have a chance to be ______________. She helped her mother with the ______________ too.

There had been time for fun during the summer too. On the weekends they went to the beach in their ______________. Sometimes they went to the concerts in the park. Audrey liked to sit in the ______________ and listen to the music. She liked to ______________ and watch as the members of the band took their bows. She had time to read, too. Whenever she read a book she liked, she would always look for other books by the same ______________. All in all it had been a very good summer for Audrey.

WORD LIST

Choose the missing word to complete each sentence.

auto	caution	audience
because	naughty	exhausted
author	August	
laundry	applaud	

NAME ______________________ DATE ____________

SUMMER ADVENTURES

During the summer Pete became so bored that he began to ________ the kind of adventure he had read about. He would have liked to explore a deep, dark ________ in a hillside. Perhaps he, too, could find a magic lamp that he would rub and a ________ would come forth to do his bidding. They would take a raft and sail out over many a high ocean ________. They would do many ________ deeds. Perhaps they could ________ some sailors who were being sold into ________ by pirates. He would send their captain to a watery ________. After he ________ the other pirates he would have them join him in some of the ________ deeds of all. Life on the ocean waves seemed much better to Pete than the city ________ where he spent his days.

WORD LIST

Choose the missing word to complete each sentence.

save	brave	forgave
cave	grave	slavery
wave	crave	bravest
slave	pavement	

NAME ______________________________ DATE ________________

A SAD MORNING

John sat on the back steps. He was so sleepy that he opened his mouth in a big ________________. He had been awake since __________ when he had heard his mother and father talking. His mother was sick, and his father had taken her to the doctor. John felt so sad that he wanted to ________________. His puppy came over and put his ________ on John's knees and licked his face. When the puppy ________________ that John didn't feel like playing, he went to chase a young ________ that he had seen in the woods. John watched the puppy. Then he looked up and saw a ________________ flying overhead. He was thirsty so he went in the house and took a glass of lemonade. He put two __________ in the glass and drank the lemonade. He sat down on the bottom step and took a stick and began ________________ circles in the sand. He was thinking of his mother and how ________________ it was that she was sick. He reached in his pocket and took out a shiny, red ____________. It tasted like ________________. He sucked on it for a while, but he didn't feel any better. Then he heard the car on the road. He ran to meet his mother and father. They told him that his mother would soon be better, if they all took good care of her.

WORD LIST

Choose the missing word to complete each sentence.

saw	straws	yawn
paws	hawk	drawing
fawn	bawl	strawberries
dawn	awful	jawbreaker

NAME ______________________________ DATE ______________

MOTHER'S BIRTHDAY

Kay sat down. She had to think. "Let's see. ______________ is Monday, the fifth ______________ in the month of ______________. The next day will be ______________, and then in two more days it will be ______________. That will be Mother's ______________." Kay ______________ tried to find a ______________ to make her Mother's birthday fun and to ______________ that she loved her. She took her paper and ______________ and made a birthday card. "______________ we can have a party and ______________ games," she said to herself. What do you like to do on your birthday?

WORD LIST

Choose the missing word to complete each sentence.

May	day	Today
play	Maybe	always
way	crayons	Tuesday
say	birthday	Thursday

NAME ______________________________ DATE ______________

A HIKE TO THE MEADOW

Tom and Bill had taken a long hike out to the grassy ____________ on the edge of town. They each had a ____________ pack on his back. They walked so far and so fast that by the time they got to the meadow they could hardly catch their ____________. They sat down on old tree stumps and watched a bird flying overhead. They saw a ________ float down from one of its wings.

They started talking about a book they had both ____________. In it some awful things had happened. Then they started talking about things that they thought would be awful.

Bill said, "Just suppose you had a really bad ____________ on a day you had a test."

Tom replied, "You know there are many people who don't have anything to eat—not even ____________."

Bill said, "How about those plants that have leaks of ____________ gas? I'd hate to live near there."

Tom chimed in, "I think it would be awful to be ____________ and not be able to hear a thing."

Bill answered, "Isn't it great that we are able to enjoy hiking to the meadow?" Then the boys were ____________ to return home.

WORD LIST

Choose the missing word to complete each sentence.

deaf	breath	headache
read	heavy	meadow
bread	ready	
feather	deadly	

NAME ______________________ DATE ______________

A HARD CHOICE

Tommy's fourth grade ____________ has given his class a term project. The children are to choose a subject and then ____________ books to learn as much as they can about it. They then are to write a report. Tommy doesn't think this will be ____________ to do. He is ____________ to do a good job because he likes to ____________ his teacher. He is having a hard time choosing one of these subjects:

The American ____________ —where it builds its nest — how and where it lives.

The ____________ crop of the western plains — how it is grown, harvested, processed, and sold.

The ____________ — how he builds dams and what effect that has on the area where he lives.

How ____________ are grown in the south and what they are used for.

Tommy does not want to ____________ his choice for the last minute. Which subject would you choose if you were Tommy?

WORD LIST

Choose the missing word to complete each sentence.

read	please	beaver
easy	leave	peanuts
eagle	wheat	
eager	teacher	

NAME ______________________________ DATE ______________

LIFE ON THE FARM

When Ted visited his grandfather and grandmother on their farm last summer one of his jobs was to feed the animals. Ted could always tell when the pigs got hungry. Just before their ______________ they started ______________. What a noise they made when they ______________.

Once when a horse hurt his leg his grandfather called the vet because the leg was not ______________ the way it should. After the vet put salve on the leg and taped it up, the leg began to ______________.

The times Ted liked best were the times he spent with his grandmother and grandfather at the kitchen table when they ate their ______________. His grandmother was a good cook and every ______________ was a ______________ treat. When he was with them he felt that the farm was where he ______________ belonged and that his life back in the city seemed ______________.

WORD LIST

Choose the missing word to complete each sentence.

meal	really	squealed
heal	healing	unreal
real	squealing	
meals	mealtime	

NAME ______________________ DATE ______________

SALLY'S NINTH BIRTHDAY

It was Sally's ninth birthday. She had gone to the ____________ with her mother to buy chocolate milk and ice ____________ for her party. Her mother had hung colored paper ____________ around the front door. Sally looked out the window and saw the ____________ reflected in the pond across the road. Sally was thinking of the wish she would make when she blew out the candles on her cake. She would wish that she'd stop having those bad ____________. Sometimes when she was ____________ she would hear a loud ____________. Then she would wake up and it would be she who was ____________. Sally hoped that if she wished hard enough her wish would come true. Then, when it got dark and she saw a ____________ reflected in the pond, she would not have to worry about being a ____________.

WORD LIST

Choose the missing word to complete each sentence.

cream	screaming	dreamer
dreams	streamers	moonbeam
scream	sunbeams	
dreaming	creamery	

NAME ______________________ DATE ______________

THE LOST EARRING

It was almost a ______________ ago that Jane got a pair of ______________ on her tenth birthday. They were very ______________ to her. When she wasn't wearing them in her ______________ she kept them in a small box on a table ______________ her bed. She had ______________ that if she was not careful she would lose them. One cold day she wore earmuffs to school. Soon after she came home, she looked in the mirror and saw that she was wearing only one earring. She looked all over the house but could not find the missing earring. How could an earring ______________ like that? Soon the ______________ were flowing down her cheeks, and she could not see ______________ enough to keep looking. Her mother tried to comfort her, but she was not willing to ______________ what her mother was saying. The next morning as she was getting ready to leave for school she found the earring stuck to her ______________. Jane was so happy. She ran downstairs to tell her mother the good news.

WORD LIST

Choose the missing word to complete each sentence.

hear	year	earrings
dear	tears	earmuff
near	fears	disappear
ears	clearly	

NAME ______________________________ DATE ______________

FOOD FOR THOUGHT

Jan likes to cook almost as much as she likes to ____________. She helps her mother shape the ____________ when her family has spaghetti for dinner. She likes to ____________ the eggs with an ____________ when her mother makes a cake. She helps to knead the good whole ____________ bread her mother makes. She knows how to season the ____________ with salt, pepper, and garlic when they have roast beef. She makes sure that the rolls are ____________ just right before she puts them on the table. Jan washes the dishes that were used in fixing dinner and puts everything away ____________ before they sit down. After everyone is ____________ at the table and has started ____________, her mother always thanks Jan for her help. Jan is happy that her mother ____________ her with love and respect.

WORD LIST

Choose the missing word to complete each sentence.

eat	treats	eating
beat	neatly	meatballs
meat	heated	eggbeater
seated	wheat	

NAME ______________________ DATE ______________

GETTING READY FOR THE PARTY

Mrs. Peck tied Jon's ______________. He had combed his hair, and his face was so clean that the ______________ on his nose showed up more than ever. Then she turned to Sue. She fastened her ______________. Mrs. Peck stood back to look at both children. She was ______________ to make sure that they were neat and that not even a ______________ of dirt was on their shoes. She said, "I have to get ready to take you to the party. I want you to stay clean and not do anything ______________ while you wait. I don't want you to look as if you had been in a ______________ when we get there. Why don't you go sit outside on the ______________ and play a game of ______________ while you wait?"

When Mrs. Peck was almost ready she looked through the window to see what the children were doing. Jon was stretching his ______________ because he didn't like the feel of the collar and necktie. While Sue was waiting for Jon to move his checker she watched a ______________ pecking in a nearby tree. Mrs. Peck was so proud of her children.

WORD LIST

Choose the missing word to complete each sentence.

neck	checkers	reckless
deck	freckles	necklace
wreck	necktie	woodpecker
speck	checking	

NAME ______________________________ DATE ______________

A SNOWY DAY

When ______________ woke up he felt that something had happened. He sat on the ______________ of his bunk ______________. Then he walked to the window. It was snowing! He called his brother, ______________, to see the snow. The wagon they had left in the yard was ______________ with snow. The snow stopped falling after lunch, and Ed and Teddy went outside to get their sleds. Ed's ______________ was blue, and Teddy's sled was ______________. They went to the hill to meet their friends, and played on the hill all afternoon. They must have slid down the hill a ______________ times. As the sun began to set and the sky grew ______________ in the west, they ______________ from their friends and started home.

WORD LIST

Choose the missing word to complete each sentence.

Ed	Teddy	parted
red	edge	reddish
bed	loaded	
sled	hundred	

NAME ______________________ DATE ______________

A HAPPY HALLOWEEN

When Mary woke up that Saturday morning at the end of October she had a ______________ that there was something special about the day. Then she remembered that it was ______________. She was glad that Halloween came on the ______________. That evening she put on her costume and placed a crown on her head. She felt that she really looked like a ______________. Then she met ______________ of her friends. They went down the ______________ asking for treats. Every time they came to a ______________ they wondered if there were a ghost behind it waiting to scare them. They did ______________ a lot of "scary-looking" costumes.

When Mary got home her mother and father were sitting in the dining room drinking ______________. Her mother looked at the candy she had and told her that she could not ______________ any candy that was not wrapped. Then she told her that she had to brush her ______________ very carefully after eating so many ______________ things. Mary was still so excited when she went to bed that it was hard for her to go to ______________.

WORD LIST

Choose the missing word to complete each sentence.

see	tree	coffee
keep	teeth	queen
sleep	feeling	Halloween
three	weekend	
street	sweet	

NAME ______________________________ DATE ______________

GOING TO THE PARADE

The circus was in town. Ellen wanted to go to the parade. Her mother said that she could go after she had studied for her ____________ test. When Ellen knew all the words she was ready to go. Then her mother said, "I don't want you to go by ____________."

Ellen answered, "I am ____________ years old. I don't see why I can't go by ____________."

Her mother replied, "You have plenty of time to ____________ a friend to come here for lunch. Then the two of you can go together."

While Ellen waited for Ann to come, she took her dirty clothes down the stairs to the ____________. When she heard the door ____________ ring, she let Ann in. Ann wanted to ____________ make the peanut butter and ____________ sandwiches for lunch. After they finished eating they went to the parade.

When the girls returned home, Ellen's mother asked what they had liked best in the parade. Ellen told her mother about a big ____________. A clown, wearing a bright ____________ suit and carrying a purple ____________, rode on his back.

WORD LIST

Choose the missing word to complete each sentence.

bell	spelling	twelve
myself	yellow	umbrella
help	cellar	elephant
jelly	yourself	telephone

NAME ______________________________ DATE ________________

A DAY IN SEPTEMBER

It was a warm day in ______________. Bill and Jim sat on the steps drinking ______________. When their glasses were ______________ they took ______________ inside. They were sad. They knew that they would not have a week off from school until Christmas came in ______________.

"I really lose my ______________ when I think about how hard I will have to work," Jim said.

Bill reminded him that he would be a ______________ of Boy Scouts this year. Then Jim remembered that they could be monitors ______________ this year. Both boys began to ______________ the things they liked about school, and September didn't seem to be such a bad month after all.

WORD LIST

Choose the missing word to complete each sentence.

them	remember	lemonade
empty	December	member
temper	September	themselves

NAME ______________________________ DATE ________________

LET'S PRETEND

Ellen and her best ______________, Sue, liked to play together. One rainy day ______________ they could not go outside they decided to play Let's ______________. Ellen started with, "Let's pretend that my cat had ______________. There are ______________ of them, and I can keep them all."

Sue decided that she'd like to have a ______________ that would lay an egg each morning for her breakfast.

______________ Ellen said, "I like to draw. Just think how nice it would be if I had so many ______________ that I would not have to stop to sharpen them. I think that ______________ would be plenty."

Sue said, "There is too long a time between Christmas and my birthday. I would like to have a ______________ every week. Just think how much fun it would be to ______________ a present every week."

Soon after that, when the rain stopped, the girls ______________ outside to play.

WORD LIST

Choose the missing word to complete each sentence.

ten	when	pencils
Then	twenty	chicken
open	kittens	present
went	Pretend	friend

NAME ______________________ DATE ______________

BOB'S SATURDAY MORNING

Last Saturday morning Bob's mother ____________ him on an errand. She asked him to mail the check for the ____________ for their apartment. She gave him ____________ cents to buy a newspaper. He rode his bike two blocks to the mail box. On his way back home he stopped and ____________ the twenty ____________ for the paper. As he crossed the street a truck ran through a red light, and Bob had an ____________. His bike was ____________, and he chipped one of his teeth. As soon as he got home his mother called the ____________ for an appointment. As he opened the door to ____________ the office, he was afraid. The dentist was ____________ with Bob and hardly hurt him at all.

WORD LIST

Choose the missing word to complete each sentence.

sent	cents	accident
rent	enter	dentist
spent	gentle	
dented	twenty	

NAME ______________________________ DATE ______________

FARM LIFE

Ellie's father is a ______________. The whole family works ________ on the farm. Her ______________ freezes and cans vegetables and fruit and keeps the farm records. Ellie and her two ________ help their mother. Ellie's ______________ is in charge of the farm. Her ______________, Tom, pumps ______________ up from the ______________ that flows along one side of their farm. This helps them to get ______________ crops. The only ______________ who does not work on the farm is Ellie's baby brother. The family works hard all spring and summer, but ______________ the crops are gathered Ellie and ______________ family find ______________ things to do just for fun. But soon ______________ spring comes, and the hard work starts all ______________ again.

WORD LIST

Choose the missing word to complete each sentence.

her	over	sisters
after	better	brother
river	father	together
water	mother	farmer
other	person	another

NAME ______________________ DATE ______________

A MATH LESSON

It was time for Tom to ______________ and get ready for school. He walked over to his ______________ where he had left his math homework. His work was a ______________. It would have been neater if he really understood the math ______________ for today. He knew that in math it was no use to try ______________ the answer. He could not get the right answer ______________ he understood the work. The only way to have ______________ in math was to know how to do the work. It was the same way when his father was teaching him to play __________. He decided to hurry and get to school early. He was sure that if he asked Miss Lester for extra help, she would say, "______________."

WORD LIST

Choose the missing word to complete each sentence.

Yes	dress	lesson
mess	unless	success
chess	desk	guessing

NAME ______________________ DATE ______________

BIRD WATCHING

Ann and Jane sat under a tree on the edge of the ____________. They watched a robin pull on a piece of straw. Jane said, "I bet she wants that straw to use in making her ____________. I get the ____________ feeling when I see the robins in the spring. I think spring is the ________ season of all."

Ann said, "I wish I could get close enough to see how she makes her nest. It must be the ____________ thing to do."

Jane asked, "Have you ever seen a humming bird? They are so tiny. I think they are the ____________ birds of all."

Ann replied, "No, I haven't, but I saw an eagle once. It was huge. It was the ____________ bird I ever saw."

Jane asked, "Have you ever watched blue jays? I saw one swoop down and dive at my cat. It was so angry. It was the ____________ bird I ever saw. Did that cat run! It ran the ____________ I ever saw it go."

WORD LIST

Choose the missing word to complete each sentence.

nest	forest	biggest
best	nicest	maddest
smallest	hardest	fastest

NAME ______________________________ DATE ________________

BETTY GOES TO THE MARKET

Betty went to the farmers' ______________ with her mother. She saw apples piled in ______________. She saw pretty, warm ______________ for the bed and a small ______________ to chop wood with. A little ______________ got out of his cage and ran through the market. His owner, who was ______________ because he ran away, went to find him. Betty wanted something to eat so her mother got her a hot ______________ with salt on it. Then she ______________ Betty pick a gift for her brother. She saw a ______________ plane on the top shelf. She had to ______________ to get it. She liked the jet ______________ than the rest of the toys. On the way home it was so ______________ in the car after the noise of the market.

WORD LIST

Choose the missing word to complete each sentence.

let	quiet	market
better	piglet	hatchet
jet	stretch	blankets
upset	pretzel	baskets

NAME ______________________ DATE ______________

SEVEN, SEVENTEEN, AND SEVENTY

Beverly is six years old. Next year she will be ____________. She has a feeling she will be smarter then. Her cousin Evelyn is ____________ years old. Beverly thinks that Evelyn is as ____________ as anyone can be. It will be ____________ more years before Beverly is seventeen. When you are six years old, ____________ you look ____________ is older than you are.

Their grandfather is ____________ years old, and he can remember when a lot of the events in the social studies books took place. Beverly wonders if she will ____________ be that old. ____________ time she asks her grandfather what it is like to be seventy, he says that you will ____________ know until you have tried it. Beverly just can't wait to see how it feels to be all grown-up.

WORD LIST

Choose the missing word to complete each sentence.

ever	never	seventeen
seven	eleven	seventy
Every	everybody	
clever	everywhere	

NAME ______________________________ DATE ______________

ON THE STEPS

Lewis sat on the front steps. He was ____________ bubble gum. He ____________ a bubble. It ____________ bigger and bigger. He ____________ that his mother did not like for him to blow bubbles. He decided to blow just a ____________ more bubbles and then he would stop. He looked at the ____________ of the trees and the distant hills. A bird ____________ overhead. Lewis went into the house to get a pad of paper and the ____________ set of colored pencils he had gotten for his birthday. He sat down and ____________ a sketch of the trees and hills. Just then the paper boy passed by and ____________ a copy of the daily ____________ on the porch. Lewis took the paper inside and gave it to his mother. He showed her the picture he had drawn. She liked it so much that she put it up in the kitchen.

WORD LIST

Choose the missing word to complete each sentence.

new	blew	chewing
few	flew	view
drew	knew	threw
grew	newspaper	

NAME ______________________ DATE ______________

LATE AFTERNOON

It was late in the afternoon when Anne rode her ______________ home. There were many ______________ on the street so she had to be careful. As soon as she came into the house she walked over to her baby sister's ______________. Sue had gotten her ______________ stuck in the mobile over the cradle. Anne helped her get loose. Then Anne made a funny face and smiled as Sue started to ______________. Anne gave Sue her toy ______________ and said, "Now you ______________ down and have your nap."

Anne walked into the kitchen and saw that the ______________ was on the stove. She knew that meant that it would soon be time for dinner. Anne did not like to be ______________ so she decided to set the ______________. She went to look for her mother to see what else she could do to help.

WORD LIST

Choose the missing word to complete each sentence.

idle
table
kettle
ankle
settle
turtle
bicycle
people
giggle
cradle

NAME ______________________ DATE ______________

THE END OF THE SCHOOL YEAR

It was June. Next week would be the beginning of ______________ from school. Susan had taken her last ______________ of the school year. She thought back over all the time she had spent in school. Her mother and father had told her that she must pay close ______________ to her work. She had learned how important it was to listen to the ________ her teacher gave for doing her work. She remembered the first time she saw the plus sign and learned how to do ____________. Later she learned about the minus sign and how to do ______________. After that the class learned that when a whole thing is divided into equal parts you have ______________. In social studies she had learned about the __________ we live in. They had paid close attention to the ____________ for president. She had read all the books on her reading list. She liked both true stories and ______________. She had worked hard this year in school. She was ready for the summer vacation.

WORD LIST

Choose the missing word to complete each sentence.

fractions	directions	subtraction
fiction	addition	examination
election	nation	
vacation	attention	

NAME ______________________________ DATE ______________

TAKING CARE OF BABY SISTER

There are many things that Sally does to help take care of her baby sister, Sue. Sally ties the ______________ around Sue's neck when it is time for Sue to eat. She feeds her small spoonfuls of food, and waits for Sue to ______________ at it. Then she wipes her face because Sue does ______________ her food. Sometimes when Sally is coloring with her crayons, Sue crawls over to ______________ on a piece of paper. When it is time to go outside Sally ties the ______________ on her cap. When it is nap time Sally puts Sue in her ______________. Sally likes to take care of her sister. It makes her feel important and all grown-up.

WORD LIST

Choose the missing word to complete each sentence.

bib	ribbon	dribble
crib	scribble	nibble

NAME ______________________________ DATE ________________

THE FOURTH OF JULY PICNIC

On the Fourth of July Tom's family always went on a ____________ at the ________________ beach. The day before Tom would go upstairs to the ________________ to get the basket and other things they needed. While his mother prepared their lunch, Tom and his father would go to the parade. Tom loved the ________________ of the band. On the way to the beach there was always a lot of ________________. Sometimes Tom felt a bit of ________________. Suppose the traffic just stopped forever? But they always got to the beach. After they had swum and eaten their lunch, Tom's mother gave him money to buy a ________________. She always took a ________________ of the whole family at the beach. Tom likes these Fourth of July picnics. He thinks of them as a birthday party for ________________.

WORD LIST

Choose the missing word to complete each sentence.

attic	panic	music
picnic	picture	popsicle
public	traffic	America

NAME ________________________ DATE ______________

RICE PUDDING FOR DESSERT

One cold afternoon Mrs. Price asked Sue what she would like for dessert that evening. Sue said, "Gingerbread with whipped cream would be ______________. Fresh strawberries would be even ______________."

Mrs. Price replied, "With ______________ so high for cream and fresh strawberries, I don't think we can have those."

Sue said, "I think your ______________ pudding would be ______________ of all."

Sue went in the kitchen to help her mother. She measured the rice carefully so none would spill and bring ______________. She asked her mother which ______________ she wanted. Her mother asked for the nutmeg and ______________. Then Sue asked which ______________ she wanted to use to mix the milk and eggs. Her mother asked for the egg-beater.

Once the rice pudding was in the oven, Sue took a ______________ of bread and a piece of cheese to eat. She peeked in the oven __________ to see if the pudding was done. When her mother took it from the oven it was golden in color and smelled spicy. Sue knew that dessert was going to be special that night.

WORD LIST

Choose the missing word to complete each sentence.

mice	slice	spices
nice	nicer	allspice
rice	prices	device
twice	nicest	

NAME ______________________________ DATE ______________

A MOTHER'S DAY PICNIC

A few days before Mother's Day ______________ looked in his piggy bank. He had four quarters, five dimes, and one ______________. What could he buy for his mother for $1.55? He talked it over with his father and his sister, Nan. Mr. Pickett said that they could plan a picnic so that their mother would not have to cook on Mother's Day. Dick could pay for the ______________ to get into the park, Nan could make the cake, and Mr. Pickett would buy the rest of the food.

On Mother's Day they left for the park early so that they could ______________ the picnic spot they liked best. Mr. Pickett started a fire in the ______________ fireplace. Nan and Dick set the table. Then they put the ______________ on the fireplace grill to cook. When it was almost done Nan ______________ set out the salads and ______________. After they finished their meal, Nan and Dick toasted marshmallows until they were golden on the outside and gooey and ______________ on the inside. Then the children joined a ______________ ball game with other children in the park. As the sun began to set they could hear a ______________ chirp in the bushes. It was then time to go home.

WORD LIST

Choose the missing word to complete each sentence.

pick	pickles	chicken
kick	sticky	tickets
Dick	quickly	cricket
brick	nickel	

NAME ______________________________ DATE ________________

A WINTER AFTERNOON

Jane and Jim took their sleds and started for the hill down the road. They came to a ______________ over a stream. They stopped in the ______________ of the bridge and looked down at the stream. It had frozen and was ______________ ice. Jim said, "I think I will jump down there. It will be fun to ______________ on the ice."

Jane answered, "You know you are not allowed to do that. Do you remember what happened when you ______________ that the last time?"

Jim replied, "Aw, you know I was only ______________."

Jane said, "I think you are ______________ when you kid like that."

Jim responded, "Oh, come on. I bet the other ______________ are already on the hill."

They ______________ down the hill on their sleds all afternoon. Soon it was time to go home. They had to walk over the bridge again on their way home.

WORD LIST

Choose the missing word to complete each sentence.

did	skid	kidding
kids	middle	solid
slid	bridge	horrid

NAME ______________________ DATE ______________

A JUNE AFTERNOON

One June afternoon Jill and Debbie ______________ that it was too nice to play ______________ the house so they went ______________ and sat on the steps.

"Shall we ask Ann and Jane to come over to play ______________-and-seek?" asked Debbie.

"No," Jill answered. "Let's ______________ our bikes to the park and play on the ______________."

On the way to the park they passed a church just as a wedding party was coming out. They saw the tall, handsome ______________ with his pretty ______________ dressed all in white at his ______________. The girls went on with their ride to the park. When they saw their friends they told them about the wedding they had seen.

WORD LIST

Choose the missing word to complete each sentence.

ride	slides	outside
side	bride	decided
hide	inside	bridegroom

NAME ______________________ DATE ______________

A SATURDAY AFTERNOON

One Saturday afternoon Bob and Ted were walking home after seeing a ______________. It had been about a ______________ who stole a treasure and then ______________ it. After they finished talking about the movie they started talking about a TV show they had seen. It was set long ago during the War of the Roses in England when two groups fought to protect their ______________. There had been a ______________ fight between two men wearing armor. The sword of one was able to __________ the ______________ of the other. What a ______________ it had been when the fight was over.

Bob reached in his pocket and took out some candy. He offered Ted a ______________. "What shall we do now?" he asked. "Do you think anyone is at the baseball ______________?" "I don't know," said Ted. "Let's go see."

The two boys walked over to see if their friends were playing ball.

WORD LIST

Choose the missing word to complete each sentence.

field	movie	pierce
thief	buried	shield
piece	relief	
beliefs	fierce	

NAME ______________________________ DATE ______________

A LOST PUPPY

Ann had taken her puppy out in the yard to play. When she went back into the house she ______________ him to a post. The puppy barked because he did not like being tied to the post. Ann's little sister, Betty, ___________ the puppy. The puppy ran out of the yard. Betty ______ to find him but could not find where he had gone.

When Ann came out she asked, "Where is my puppy?"

Betty ______________, "I don't know." When Ann asked how the puppy had gotten loose, Betty was not sure what to say. She knew that if she ______________ to Ann and ______________ that she had untied the puppy that it would not be right. As she told Ann what she had done, Betty ______________ because she was so sad. Soon she __________ her tears and the two girls went to look for the puppy together.

WORD LIST

Choose the missing word to complete each sentence.

lied	cried	denied
tied	untied	replied
dried	tried	

NAME ______________________ DATE ______________

A DAY IN THE COUNTRY

Last summer Pam and Andy went camping with their family. One morning they made a ____________ climb up a mountain until they came to the foot of a steep ____________. Andy said that ________ Pam hadn't been with him he would have climbed the cliff. After all, Andy was ____________ years old, and Pam was only ten. Since Pam could not make the climb, they decided to return to camp. On the way down they chose a ____________ path from the one they had taken on the way up. It was a lot safer.

Late in the afternoon they took a rowboat out on the lake and ________ with the current. They could ____________ the sweet smell of honeysuckle on the shore. Then the wind would ____________, and they got a ____________ of hamburgers cooking over a campfire. That was when they knew it was dinner time. They made a ________ trip back to camp.

WORD LIST

Choose the missing word to complete each sentence.

if	whiff	difficult
sniff	cliff	drifted
shift	fifteen	
swift	different	

NAME ______________________________ DATE ______________

A PIG AND SOME PIGLETS

Pete had never been on a farm before. He liked to sit on the fence around the pen and watch the ______________. It was so fat and ______________. The pig would roll around and ______________ in the mud near its drinking water. There were four little ______________ in the pen. One of them was very small, but the other three were so much ______________. They ran around the yard in a ______________ path. They liked ______________ in the mud too. Whenever the smallest piglet would ______________ under a branch that had fallen from a tree a ______________ would break off and hit her in the face. Every time Pete saw this he would laugh and ______________.

WORD LIST

Choose the missing word to complete each sentence.

pig	wiggle	piglets
big	bigger	giggle
dig	zigzag	
twig	digging	

NAME ______________________ DATE ______________

A NIGHTMARE

It was almost midnight last ____________ when Jane woke up. She was crying. She had had a ____________. She called her mother and told her how she felt. Her mother said, "I know how much a nightmare can ____________ you, but it is only a dream. Things seem more scary during the ____________. Look out your window at the ________. See how ____________ it is."

Jane asked, "Will you leave the ____________ on in the hall? Please don't close my door ____________ so I can see the light."

Her mother said that would be all ____________. Then she kissed Jane and said, "Sleep well and ____________." As her mother went back to her own room Jane felt better and quickly fell back to sleep.

WORD LIST

Choose the missing word to complete each sentence.

night	right	nighttime
light	goodnight	nightmare
tight	frighten	
bright	moonlight	

NAME ______________________________ DATE ______________

SUNDAY AT THE ZOO

Ted always looked forward to the Sunday mornings when he went to the zoo with his father. As soon as they went through the ____________ at the entrance he went to the ____________ building. Outside of the building was a shallow pool with low ____________ of rock at one end and ____________ all around it. On the edge of the pool was a huge ____________. Its mouth was so big, Ted wondered what it would look like if it ____________. The crocodile did not ________. It did not move at all ____________ Ted stood there, but he knew it could move very quickly when it wanted to. After they had looked at the other animals Ted's father said, "It's time to start for home. You know we have to walk almost a ____________, and we don't want to be late for lunch. We can come back to the zoo next week."

WORD LIST

Choose the missing word to complete each sentence.

tile	piles	smiled
mile	while	crocodile
smile	reptile	turnstile

NAME ______________________________ DATE ______________

A DAY IN BED

There was a girl named ______________. She did not like to be sick and stay home from school. Every time she had an ______________ her mother would fluff up her ______________ and pull the warm, puffy ______________ up high under her chin. Her mother would bring Jill fruit juice and warm ______________ with honey to drink. Jill liked to run her hand over the quilt and feel how ______________ it was to touch. She would close her eyes, lie very ______________, and pretend.

She liked to pretend that she had climbed a ______________. When she had come to the ______________ she would lie down and rest. She would stay there ______________ she was well rested.

When Jill stopped pretending she could hear the ______________ on their way home from school. Then she would think, "Perhaps tomorrow I ______________ feel better and be able to go to school too."

WORD LIST

Choose the missing word to complete each sentence.

hill	until	milk
still	pillow	silky
will	illness	quilt
Jill	hilltop	children

NAME ______________________________ DATE ______________

KIM'S STAY AT CAMP

When ______________ came home from boy scout camp his mother asked ______________ what he liked best there. He told her that the most ______________ thing was that he had learned to __________. He told her of the fireplace that they had made. He had made the __________ by ______________. He told her of sitting at the ________ of the pond when the sun was setting and the light was getting ______________. He told her of an ______________ in his bunk who had tied the laces of his sneakers together. Then he asked if he could go back to camp next summer.

WORD LIST

Choose the missing word to complete each sentence.

dim	Kim	himself
rim	imp	chimney
him	swim	important

NAME ____________________ DATE ____________

THE TWINS' CABIN

The Linton ____________ had a little ____________ in their back yard. In the cold ____________ they liked to play ____________ of the cabin. They pretended that ____________ passed their way ____________ a hunting party and they would invite them to come ____________ the cabin. In spring they looked out their ____________ and saw the first ____________ looking for dry grass so she could ____________ to make her nest. They liked to stay in the cabin until their mother called them for dinner. They always answered, "We will be there in a ____________," and made sure they were.

WORD LIST

Choose the missing word to complete each sentence.

in	robin	inside
twins	winter	window
into	Indians	minute
cabin	begin	

NAME ______________________________ DATE ______________

A SHOPPING TRIP

Yesterday Sue and her mother went downtown to go shopping. They were trying to ______________ a new jacket for Sue. As they were starting to cross the street they saw a ______________ man waiting to cross. Sue's mother asked if she could help him. He said, "It would be very ______________ of you."

Sue walked ______________ her mother as they crossed the street. After they left the man, Sue asked, "Didn't you feel strange helping someone you don't know?"

Sue's mother answered, "No, I never ______________ helping someone who needs help. An act of ______________ always makes me feel good. After we find your jacket will you ______________ me that I want to look for some yarn? I hope that they have the kind of skeins that ______________ as you use them. I do not like to have to ______________ the yarn into balls before I can start knitting."

Then they went to look for a jacket for Sue.

WORD LIST

Choose the missing word to complete each sentence.

wind	kind	remind
mind	blind	unwind
find	behind	kindliness

NAME ______________________ DATE ______________

WHAT DO YOU LIKE BEST?

Jane's teacher asked her class to make a list of the __________ they liked best. She said that they could list __________ at all. Here are some of the things that were listed:

Joe liked __________ a baseball game.
Ann liked __________ in the chorus.
Jim liked sleeping late in the __________.
Sue liked __________ to the circus.
Debbie liked her __________ cap and scarf.
Connie liked her new gold __________.
Tony liked __________ able to go barefoot in the mud when it was __________.
Jan liked the candy her father __________ home.
Jeff liked __________ broken toys.
Name __________ you like.

WORD LIST

Choose the missing word to complete each sentence.

ring	morning	anything
brings	singing	matching
things	raining	something
going	winning	
being	fixing	

NAME ______________________________ DATE ______________

A SHOPPING TRIP

After dinner Mrs. Dinkins said to Susan, "I have been ____________ that it is time for us to go shopping for a new sweater for you and a present for Ann's birthday." At the store the only sweater Susan saw that she liked was a pretty ____________ one. Her mother read the tag on the sweater. She said, "This sweater will ____________ if it is not washed by hand. Then it has to be spread out flat and smooth so there are no ____________. Would you rather look for a sweater that we can put in the washer?"

Without a ____________ of her eyes Susan said, "I ____________ I can wash it myself if you show me how. Let's take this one."

When they passed the jewelry counter Susan said, "Let's see if we can find a pretty ____________ for Ann's birthday. I think that she would like that bracelet."

As they came near the soda fountain they heard the ____________ of glasses. Mrs. Dinkins said, "I am very thirsty. Let's have something to ____________."

When they left the store to go home, they saw that it was dark and that the stars were ____________ in the sky. They had no idea that they had been in the store for such a long time.

WORD LIST

Choose the missing word to complete each sentence.

pink	blink	shrink
clink	trinket	twinkling
think	thinking	
drink	wrinkles	

NAME ______________________________ DATE ____________

AFTERNOON IN THE PARK

Mary sat on the park bench and took a small ____________ of lemonade. She held the straw between her ____________. When there was no lemonade left she walked over to the zoo, being careful not to ____________ over the high curb. She saw a small ____________ looking for something to eat near the monkeys' cage. Then she went to the pool where she watched the seals move their ____________ without any effort as they swam. She stood on ____________ to watch them reach for the fish the keeper gave them. They were ____________ wet as they jumped for the fish. The walk was wet and ____________ near the pool. She was careful not to ____________. Then she walked over to the garden where the spring flowers were in bloom. The one she liked best was a big, red ____________. She took one last look at the tulips and started on her way home.

WORD LIST

Choose the missing word to complete each sentence.

lips	tulip	slippery
sip	flippers	chipmunk
trip	dripping	
slip	tiptoe	

NAME ________________________ DATE ____________

LEE'S BIRTHDAY PARTY

Lee's mother and father gave her a big party for her tenth __________. They invited __________ of her friends to come to the party. The party was held outside near the big __________ tree. When all the __________ had arrived they played games. They had a treasure hunt __________. Then they played hide and seek. When it was time to eat they sat in a big __________ on the grass. They ate ice cream and cake. They drank a lot of punch because they were __________. Then Lee opened her presents. She was given a pretty __________ with long sleeves, two __________ with belts at the waist, a stuffed __________ with a long fluffy tail, and a toy __________ that sang when she pulled a string. Lee was so happy. She couldn't thank her parents and friends enough.

WORD LIST

Choose the missing word to complete each sentence.

fir	shirt	birthday
bird	skirts	squirrel
girls	thirty	thirsty
first	circle	

NAME ______________________________ DATE ________________

FRED'S GRANDFATHER

Fred was sitting near the ______________ with his grandfather. As they watched the blazing ______________ they talked about his grandfather's plans to ______________ from his job. Fred's grandfather told him about the different jobs he had had.

He said, "When I was your age I had a great ______________ to be a ______________. When I went to the fire department they told me I was too young for them to ______________ me. I still ______________ firemen and the brave work they do. When I was older I started playing baseball in high school. Then I wanted to be an ______________. During the summer I worked in an auto supply store and sold ______________. Sometimes I would even change a ______________ when they were busy in the shop. I finally decided that I wanted to work in a factory. I like being the foreman at the ______________ factory. When I see all the wire on those big spools I feel proud, but now it is time for me to retire."

WORD LIST

Choose the missing word to complete each sentence.

fire	tires	fireplace
wire	admire	umpire
hire	desire	fireman
tire	retire	

NAME ______________________ DATE ______________

MAKE A WISH

The children were playing outside after dinner when they saw the first star in the evening sky. They all made a ______________ on the star. Here are the ______________ they made when they ______________ on the star:

Ted wished he could go ______________ whenever he wanted to and that he would always catch a big ______________.

Jane wished that she did not have to help wash the ______________ after dinner.

Alan wished that his mother would not ______________ him when he left his homework at school.

Mary wished her mother did not think she was ______________ when she did not let her little sister play with her dolls.

Jim wished he did not have to take the ______________ out to the trash can every day.

Tom wished that his teacher did not think he was ______________ when he made a mistake.

What would you wish for?

WORD LIST

Choose the missing word to complete each sentence.

wish	punish	foolish
fish	wished	rubbish
wishes	selfish	
dishes	fishing	

NAME ______________________ DATE ______________

GETTING READY FOR CHRISTMAS

It had been a warm day for December, just three days before __________. The night air was cold, and a __________ was rising from the ground. Inside the house it was warm. Mrs. Lister had been baking __________ cookies all afternoon. Then she had baked a pan of __________ to have with the chicken for dinner.

After dinner Mrs. Lister sat down to check her __________ of the things she still had to do. She did not want to __________ doing anything she had planned. While she was working at her desk, Mr. Lister, together with Paul, and his __________, Kim, decided it was time to hang the __________. They hung sprigs of it over the doorways. While they were hanging the mistletoe Paul began to __________ "Jingle Bells." When Mrs. Lister came to the doorway to see what they were doing, they each gave her a big __________.

WORD LIST

Choose the missing word to complete each sentence.

miss	crisp	mistletoe
list	sister	Christmas
kiss	whistle	
mist	biscuits	

NAME ______________________________ DATE ____________________

MITCH'S PETS

When Mitch moved from the ______________ he wanted a pet. His mother said he could have a ______________. He had a hard time thinking of a name for her and ended up calling her ______________. His mother gave him a small ______________ to put milk in to pour into Kitty's dish. One cool spring morning Mitch put on his ______________ and went out to play with Kitty. Mitch went to ______________ on his swing. Soon he saw Kitty ______________ something and went to see what it was. There was a baby ______________ with long ears. It was so ______________! Mitch picked it up. It ______________ Mitch's finger. It wanted something to eat. "It would be fun to have a rabbit for a pet too," Mitch said to Kitty as he went to look for food.

WORD LIST

Choose the missing word to complete each sentence.

sit	city	kitten
bit	hitting	mittens
Kitty	pitcher	
rabbit	little	

NAME ______________________________ DATE ________________

FIRST TIME AT CAMP

The first time Bill went away to Boy Scout camp he was very __________. His mother had told him to be ______________ to his leaders and to be sure to ______________ to her and tell her what he was doing.

It was ______________ a long trip to the ______________. The first evening they set up their camp. Then Bill helped gather the wood for the campfire. He watched one of the older boys ______________ the fire. As their dinner was cooking, Bill was so hungry that he could hardly wait to take the first ______________ of his hamburger. As it got late the moon looked big and ______________ in the dark sky.

The next morning after breakfast each boy made his own __________ out of paper and splints of wood. After lunch as Bill ____________ to his mother he tells her about what he has been doing and that he has been behaving ______________.

WORD LIST

Choose the missing word to complete each sentence.

kite	polite	politely
bite	quite	ignite
white	writes	campsite
write	excited	

NAME ______________________ DATE ______________

SUMMER ON A FARM

Last summer John visited his aunt and uncle on their farm. His Aunt Ellen has a big kitchen with both a gas stove and a ______________ stove. After eating his ______________ for breakfast John would go out to the barn and feed the ______________. Sometimes he would ride the tractor with his uncle through the field where the ______________ were growing. On market days he would help his uncle in ______________ his truck with fruit and vegetables. On a hot afternoon he liked to walk in the shade of a forest of ______________ as he went down to the pond. Then he would get in the ______________ and row out to the middle of the pond. He enjoyed just sitting in the ______________. It was fun just to be ______________ along. Sometimes when he got back to the house his aunt would be ______________ some ribs of beef for their dinner. John thought that last summer on the farm was the best vacation ever.

WORD LIST

Choose the missing word to complete each sentence.

oats	goats	rowboat
boat	floating	loading
oaks	roasting	
coal	oatmeal	

NAME ______________________ DATE ____________

HOMEWORK, A HOBBY AND A JOB

A boy named ____________ sat at his desk. He finished the last math ____________ he had for homework. He liked school work all right, but he enjoyed his ____________ of drawing more. He took out his sketch pad and looked at some of the drawings he had done. There was one of a ____________ pecking at a corn ____________. He liked the one of the ____________ chasing a rabbit. At Halloween he had drawn a picture of a strange looking ____________. There was a ____________ hanging in the corner of the picture. The sketch Bobby liked best was the one of a boy about to ____________ a ball across the net in a tennis match. Then Bobby looked at the clock and saw it was time to start for his ____________ as a newspaper boy. So, he put away his drawings and got ready for work.

WORD LIST

Choose the missing word to complete each sentence.

job	robin	hobby
cob	goblin	problem
lob	cobweb	
Bobby	bobcats	

NAME ______________________________ DATE ______________

GETTING READY FOR BED

Every night Nan helped her little brother, Bill, get ready for bed. She made sure that he emptied each of his ______________ before he put his pants in the hamper. She did not let him leave his dirty ______________ on the floor. Together they put away his finger paints, and Bill hung up the ______________ he wore when he painted. Bill took down the fort he had built and put his ______________ in the wooden ______________ his father had made for them. He put his toy ______________ ship in the locker too. His favorite toy was his ______________ horse. Nan let him ______________ for a little while before he got in bed. When he was in bed their father and mother would ______________ on the door and come in to kiss him good night. Then Nan would go to her room to wind her __________ and get ready for bed. She liked to hear the ______________ of the clock while she was waiting to fall asleep.

WORD LIST

Choose the missing word to complete each sentence.

rock	clock	rocket
socks	rocking	locker
smock	knock	tick-tock
blocks	pockets	

NAME ______________________________ DATE ______________

WHAT TO DO?

A boy named ____________ sat on the porch of the ____________ where he was staying. He had just finished putting together a ____________ plane. He looked across the lawn and saw a little ____________ running after a butterfly. There were some girls playing ____________ ball in the field. He was trying to decide what he wanted to do. He thought he heard ____________ call his name. Then he saw his father and his ____________ coming. They were going fishing. They hoped to catch some ____________ for dinner and asked if Todd would like to come with them.

He began to ____________ his head as he said, "Yes, that is what I will do. It is ____________ that you should ask just when I was wondering what to do."

WORD LIST

Choose the missing word to complete each sentence.

odd	toddler	somebody
nod	codfish	godfather
Todd	model	
dodge	lodge	

NAME ______________________________ DATE ______________

A FOGGY DAY

It was a damp, ______________ day. Marty decided to go ______________ anyway. He tried to ______________ every day. His ______________, Rags, always ran with him. As he ran the ground felt ______________ under his feet. He wore ______________ to protect his eyes. He could see that the ______________ had settled over the city in the valley. He passed a ______________ working in the forest. As he came to a farm he saw a ______________ digging in the mud. He went on to the pond where he liked to stop for a rest. He watched a ______________ swimming in the water. He heard a ______________ croak. Then he turned to Rags and said, "Come on, Rags. It's time to go home."

WORD LIST

Choose the missing word to complete each sentence.

dog	smog	jogging
hog	foggy	goggles
jog	soggy	polliwog
frog	logger	

NAME ________________________________ DATE ________________

JIM'S CAR

Ted went out to ______________ his big brother, Jim, in the driveway. Jim had an old car on which he was always working. He had drained the ______________ out of the car into a large metal ________ pan. Jim wiped his hands on an ______________ rag. His tee shirt was ______________ with sweat. When he saw Ted he said, ''Don't you come too close. I don't want you to ______________ your clothes.'' He put the clean oil in and started the car. Jim said, ''I think it sounds too ______________.'' He picked up a screwdriver and ______________ it at the engine. ''Let's see if I can quiet it down a bit,'' he said. Soon the two boys heard the ______________ of some of Jim's friends coming down the street. Soon they all were helping Jim work on his car.

WORD LIST

Choose the missing word to complete each sentence.

oil	soil	noisy
join	foil	pointed
oily	voices	moist

NAME ______________________________ DATE ______________

A COLD MORNING

It was the first cold morning of fall. As soon as he ______________ Jim knew that it had gotten colder. After he ate breakfast his mother ______________ to him and asked if he would make a fire in the fireplace. Jim ______________ the kindling into small pieces and set them in the fireplace with wood and paper. After he lit the match and started the fire he watched the ______________ rise up the chimney. Then he ______________ at the wood with the ______________. He wanted to stir the fire so that it would not ______________ out for lack of air. After a few ______________ of the poker the fire was blazing. Just then the door bell rang. It was Bill. Bill said, "I have been waiting for you at the ball park for fifteen minutes. Why are you such a ______________ today?" Jim said he was sorry for being late. Then the two boys went out to play ball.

WORD LIST

Choose the missing word to complete each sentence.

choke	spoke	strokes
poked	awoke	smoke
broke	poker	slowpoke

NAME ________________________________ DATE ________________

ANN'S GRANDMOTHER

Ann's grandmother was getting ____________. Her hair was once the color of ____________, but now it was white. Ann liked to visit her grandmother. She ____________ such good stories. On a ________ winter day she would ____________ Ann on her lap, and they would watch the ____________ swimming in their bowl. Sometimes Ann helped her by ____________ the laundry. In the spring Ann helped her plant ____________ in her garden. Even when Ann spilled the seeds her grandmother did not ____________ her. Ann had such a good time with her grandmother that she didn't think she would mind getting ____________ when she grew up.

WORD LIST

Choose the missing word to complete each sentence.

old	gold	goldfish
cold	older	marigolds
hold	scold	
told	folding	

NAME ______________________________ DATE ______________

A STREET CHASE

Jane sat on the front steps. She was sucking on a sweet, red __________. Her __________ was on her lap, and her __________ dog, Lassie, was at her side. She had a __________ in her pocket and she was trying to decide whether to save it or spend it. Just then a __________ car passed by. A man was __________ it. He was running fast trying to catch up. He was __________ at the motor man, but Jane could not understand what he was saying. Lassie started to get up. Jane knew she wanted to __________ the man and the trolley car. Jane got up and tied her leash to a good, __________ post. Then she was not able to get __________ in the chase down the street.

WORD LIST

Choose the missing word to complete each sentence.

doll	collie	hollering
follow	solid	involved
dollar	following	
lollipop	trolley	

NAME ______________________ DATE ______________

A LONG SUMMER

When school closed Sue knew that she had the __________ summer ahead of her. There was so much she wanted to do.

Sue had __________ in the reading group at the library. She planned to read many books.

She had been a __________ of stamps for over a year. She decided that she would __________ in a stamp club, also.

When the fireman's fair came to town she would go there with her parents. The __________ coaster was the ride she liked best.

She and her friends would go to the park and __________ through the zoo. She always felt sorry for the __________ bear as he tried to keep cool in summer.

Sometimes she and her family would drive out to her uncle's farm. She liked to watch the young __________ as they ran across the field.

Sue liked to go bowling. She enjoyed watching her ball __________ down the lane toward the pins. Sue was sure that this was going to be a great summer!

WORD LIST

Choose the missing word to complete each sentence.

colts	polar	rolling
roller	enroll	enrolled
whole	stroll	collector

NAME ______________________________ DATE ______________

TOM'S TROMBONE

There was a boy named ____________. Last fall when he started playing in the school band he made a ____________ to his mother and father that he would practice on his ____________ every day. He did not like to ____________ but there were times when he would much rather be in the ____________ of his friends than practicing alone in his room. He knew he shouldn't ____________ his parents with the parents of his friends, but he did wish that they were not so strict. Still there was some ____________ in the fact that his music teacher said that he was playing very well. He decided that he would ____________ his practice. Then he would go ____________ his room and join his friends.

WORD LIST

Choose the missing word to complete each sentence.

Tom	company	comfort
from	compare	complete
promise	complain	trombone

NAME ______________________ DATE ______________

THE LAST DAY AT CAMP

On the last night at camp the two girls, ______________ and ______________, sat near the fishing ______________. During the afternoon there had been a ______________ to see who could swim best. Now they were listening to a ______________ of camp songs. They could feel the warmth of the ______________ that was blazing on the shore. The two girls did not look at all alike. Donna was tall and dark. Bonnie was small and ______________. Yet they had become very ______________ of each other during the past weeks. When the concert was over they walked to their bunk which was ______________ the ball field. They took the ______________ of their lockers and dumped them ______________ their cots. Then they started to pack so they would be ready to leave in the morning. They knew they would miss each other, but promised to write.

WORD LIST

Choose the missing word to complete each sentence.

fond	blond	Bonnie
upon	bonfire	contents
pond	beyond	contest
Donna	concert	

NAME ______________________________ DATE ______________

A LONESOME TIME

Ed Jones crossed the street ______________ and walked to the candy store. He spent all the money he had for an ice cream ________. He licked the ice cream but it did not help him feel better. He felt so ______________ since his best friend, Tom, had moved. Ed had hoped that Tom's family would ______________ the move forever, but they had moved last week. Ed's sister had said that with time he would not feel so ______________. Ed just got angry and told her that was a lot of __________. His mother had said that he could ______________ Tom on his birthday, but talking on the ______________ was not the same as having a friend next door. Ed walked over to the playground and sat on a ______________ wall while he finished his ice cream. Then he walked over to the ball field to see if any of his other friends were there.

WORD LIST

Choose the missing word to complete each sentence.

cone	lonely	baloney
phone	alone	telephone
stone	postpone	lonesome

NAME ______________________________ DATE ______________

TELEVISION OR PING-PONG?

Ed had been watching television for a ______________ time. He was watching the ____________ ____________ when Tim came to his house to play. Tim did not want to watch TV. He said, "We ______________ to the Boys' Club. Let's go there and play ______________."

Ed answered, "I want to watch this a little bit ______________. I want to hear her finish singing this ______________."

Tim replied, "What's the use of ______________ to the club if we don't go there? I think it's ______________ to sit in front of the TV all the time."

Just then the song ended, and the two boys left the house. As they walked ______________ the street to the club they heard a __________ singing in a tree. Tim said, "That bird sings better than the woman on TV did." Ed smiled and said he was right.

WORD LIST

Choose the missing word to complete each sentence.

song	belong	Ping-pong
long	along	Gong Show
wrong	belonging	
longer	songbird	

NAME ______________________________ DATE ________________

A TRIP TO THE ZOO

As soon as Nan got home from ______________ she went into the ______________ to wash her hands. Then she went into the kitchen to look for some ______________. Her mother was in the kitchen. Nan asked if they could go to the park and visit the ______________. Her mother said, "I can't go now, but we can leave ______________. Why don't you call Mary? Maybe she would like to go ______________."

When they got to the park, first they stopped at the children's zoo, which had farm animals. Both girls liked the big, gray ______________. Then they went on to see the ______________, who was eating a banana. Before they left the park Nan's mother bought each of the girls a ______________ on a string. As they walked home it started to get dark. They could see the ______________ in the evening sky. It was such a beautiful sight.

WORD LIST

Choose the missing word to complete each sentence.

too	goose	balloon
soon	school	bathroom
zoo	food	
moon	baboon	

NAME ______________________ DATE ______________

COOKERY

Jane's mother spends a lot of time in her kitchen because she likes to ____________. Mrs. Brooke has many cookbooks on a __________ in the hallway. On a kitchen shelf she has a row of cookbooks held by a ____________. She is always on the ____________ for new recipes. Sometimes she borrows cookbooks from the ____________ that parks near their house. Sometimes she finds a ____________ of recipes at the supermarket.

Jane's father likes to cook too. He always does the cooking when they have a ____________ in the park. They like to picnic near the ________ where they can hear the splashing of the water.

Janes thinks that ____________ is a good hobby. She wants to learn how to cook herself. She always stands near her mother and father so that she can ____________ at what they are doing when they cook. She thinks this is the best way for her to learn all about cooking.

WORD LIST

Choose the missing word to complete each sentence.

cook	cookout	bookend
look	lookout	cookery
brook	bookmobile	
bookshelf	booklet	

NAME ______________________ DATE ______________

POPCORN AND LOLLIPOPS

Tommy Hopper liked to play baseball after school. He was the __________ on his team. When it was time to __________ playing he went to the playground to find his sister. She was playing __________ with her friends. It was getting late, and they were just __________ when he came. They were both hungry so they stopped at a candy shop. Tommy took the __________ off the candy bin. He was a careful __________, and it took some time for him to choose a __________ for himself and one for his sister. "When we get home," he said, "I will __________ some wood. Then I will make a fire and we can __________ some good, fluffy __________ to eat."

WORD LIST

Choose the missing word to complete each sentence.

top	stopping	hopscotch
pop	shopper	shortstop
chop	popcorn	
stop	lollipop	

NAME ______________________ DATE ______________

A SAD DAY FOR NAN

It was still early in the ____________. Nan had eaten ________ flakes for breakfast. Then she had had toast and an egg. She had put the dishes and the knife, ____________, and spoon in the sink. Then she went out on the ____________ to sit while she peeled an ________ and ate it. She saw a man leading a ____________ out to a field. She picked up an ____________ that had fallen from the oak tree. She threw the acorn as far as she could. She was feeling sad. She thought it was ____________ that her grandmother had to leave so soon. In just a ____________ time her mother would take her grandmother to the ____________. Her grandmother had stayed with them ____________ a week. She had told Nan a ____________ every night at bedtime. Now it was time for her to leave. Nan hoped her grandmother would come again soon.

WORD LIST

Choose the missing word to complete each sentence.

for	story	orange
corn	horse	morning
fork	short	horrid
porch	acorn	airport

NAME ________________________ DATE ______________

SUMMER AT THE SEASHORE

Every summer Sally and her family spend a week at the ____________. Sally likes that week ____________ than any other time in the whole year. In the mornings she helps her mother with the ____________ in the cabin so they can leave for the beach as soon as possible. Sometimes she goes to the ____________ to buy bread and milk. They take their lunch to a quiet place on the ____________ and spend the rest of the day there. Sally helps her mother put out the picnic lunch. When everyone has finished eating and can't eat ____________ they rest in the shade of their umbrella before going for a swim. Sally likes to look for driftwood that has washed ____________. Sometimes she pretends that she is an ____________ who has just landed on this distant shore and that it is her job to ____________ this strange place. When she finds an old apple ____________ or the ashes from a cook-out she remembers that many people have been here ____________ her.

WORD LIST

Choose the missing word to complete each sentence.

core	shore	explorer
more	before	anymore
store	ashore	seashore
chores	explore	

NAME ______________________ DATE ______________

A WALK TO THE PARK

Bobby let his sister, Ellen, take his hand as they stood near the __________ on a busy street waiting to walk __________ the street. They waited for the green light. As they were __________ the street Ellen watched for cars coming around the corner. After they had __________ the street Bobby pulled his hand away. He was glad that Ellen took him to the park when their mother was busy, but he thought that she was too __________ when she told him what to do. There were times when he told her that she was not his __________. They walked into the park and went to a cool, green, __________ hill. Ellen __________ her big, red ball to Bobby and he tossed it back. After they had been __________ the ball for a while Ellen said it was time to go home. When they went back across the street Bobby held her hand again.

WORD LIST

Choose the missing word to complete each sentence.

boss	bossy	tossed
mossy	tossing	crosswalk
across	crossing	crossed

NAME ______________________ DATE ______________

WAITING FOR THE MAIL

Patty waited outside for the mailman ____________ every day. She sat on the fence near the ____________. The mail box was on a ____________ nearby. ____________ of the mail was for her mother and father. Their mail was ____________ ads that they threw away. Last week Patty had gotten a ____________ from her grandmother who was visiting a friend. Her grandmother's ____________ had sent her a note too. Patty had written her grandmother and her friend and had ____________ the letters the same day. She felt it was almost time for a reply. So, she waited every day for the mailman to come, hoping to hear from her grandmother.

WORD LIST

Choose the missing word to complete each sentence.

Most	posted	postcard
post	mostly	hostess
almost	gatepost	

NAME ______________________________ DATE ________________

A GIRL NAMED DOTTY

There was a girl named ______________. She was a good girl but she often ______________ things. She did ______________ keep her mind on what she was doing. When she put the ______________ with water on the stove to get ______________, she forgot it. It got ________ and hotter, but she forgot all about it. When she drank soda pop from a ______________, she forgot to be careful and ______________ her dress. Sometimes she left her lunch in her desk until it would ________. When she sewed she forgot how to hold the needle, and she ____________ the thread all tangled in ______________. Do you know anyone like Dotty?

WORD LIST

Choose the missing word to complete each sentence.

got	knots	teapot
hot	Dotty	bottle
rot	hotter	spotted
not	forgot	

NAME ________________________ DATE ____________

A CABIN IN THE MOUNTAINS

Last summer Don's family rented a cabin high in the ____________. They liked to rent one on the ____________ side of the mountain because it was sunnier there. On the first morning they were there Don went ____________ the front door and stood on the front porch. It was so nice to be ____________ in the cool, morning air. He looked as far as he could see. He was able to ____________ only three other ____________ along the side of the mountain. That afternoon they went to Echo Point. Don opened his ____________ wide to give a good ____________. His shout was so ____________ it surprised him. In just a few seconds he could hear his echo. After that they went swimming in the lake ____________ a mile from their cabin. On the way back to the cabin Don told his parents, "I really do like ____________ vacation this year."

WORD LIST

Choose the missing word to complete each sentence.

our	about	mouth
out	shout	outside
loud	count	mountains
south	houses	

NAME ______________________________ DATE ______________

A LOST BALL

The girls had been playing jacks. Nan missed catching the ball on the ____________, and the ball rolled into the tall grass that ____________ them. They looked all ____________ the area but did not find the ball.

"Where could that little, ____________ ball have gone?" asked Sue.

"It does ____________ me," answered Nan.

The girls kept looking. They heard the ____________ of traffic from the streets. They heard the ____________ noise of men repairing the street. They looked for a long time. At last they ____________ the ball on the ____________ under a small bush. They felt so silly that it had taken them so long to find the ball.

WORD LIST

Choose the missing word to complete each sentence.

found	ground	pounding
round	around	confound
sounds	rebound	surrounded

NAME ______________________ DATE ______________

SUMMER DAYS

Ted Stover looked forward to the summer days when his family went on a picnic. They put their lunch in the car and ____________ out to a small ____________ on the lake. They found a shady spot where the ____________ grew. The sun was ____________ head, but it was cool in the shade. As Ted waded out into the lake he watched as some boys ____________ off the raft. After they had a swim, they used their grill for a ____________ to broil their hot dogs. Ted's dog, ____________, came out from under the tree as soon as he smelled the hot dogs. After they ate the hot dogs and salad, they had watermelon and spice cake flavored with ____________. Ted was so full he could barely get up.

WORD LIST

Choose the missing word to complete each sentence.

cove	dove	stove
over	cloves	clover
Rover	drove	

NAME ______________________ DATE ______________

A SPRING NIGHT

Ed looked out the ______________ of his room. It seemed just a few weeks ago it had been cold and ______________. Now spring had come and the days were warm. Far ______________ in the moonlight he could see the funny old ______________ in the garden. Then he looked at the front lawn. "How can that grass ______________ so fast?" he asked himself. "I just cut it. I just ______________ I am going to have to cut it again ______________. I'm glad that Dad bought that new ______________. It sure makes it a lot easier."

He got in bed and pulled his ______________ up so he could read for a while. He leaned on his ______________ and read until he was sleepy. Then he turned off the lamp and fell asleep thinking of all the work he had to do tomorrow.

WORD LIST

Choose the missing word to complete each sentence.

grow	pillow	tomorrow
know	elbow	lawnmower
snowy	window	
below	scarecrow	

NAME ______________________ DATE ______________

COWBOY LIFE

Better than anything else, Mike liked stories and movies about the old west and the life the ____________ led. He liked the way they dressed in their ____________ leather boots and hats with wide brims. He thought it would be great to live where you could hear the ____________ of wild animals and where the dust of the range was fine as ____________. He had heard that when the cactus was in ____________ it was a fine thing to see. He knew he could not do anything about such a life ____________. He wondered ____________ he could go west when he was older. He even called his food "____________," and instead of hello, he said "____________." When his sister heard this, she just told him to stop ____________ around. To Mike, being a cowboy was serious business.

WORD LIST

Choose the missing word to complete each sentence.

how	howl	cowboys
now	powder	clowning
brown	flower	
chow	howdy	

NAME ______________________________ DATE ______________

THE CLUB

Ever since he first joined the ____________ Scouts, Bob had been in one ____________ or another. During the summer he and his friends had started a club. Most of his friends were thin, but two of the boys were ____________. The boys met at the bandstand in the ________ park. They called it their ____________. It was not far from a ____________ station. There was always noise and ____________ there. Sometimes they each worked on a model plane or ____________. Once they helped the park workers ____________ a wall that people had written on. The boys met at the clubhouse whenever they could. After dinner they stayed until it was time to go home. When they got home each boy would take a bath in the ____________. Then they would get ready for bed and dream about what they would do the next day.

WORD LIST

Choose the missing word to complete each sentence.

tub	chubby	clubhouse
Cub	public	submarine
club	subway	
scrub	hubbub	

NAME ______________________________ DATE ________________

A DAY IN APRIL

It was April. Every tulip had at least one ______________. It had been sunny all day, but then there was a ______________ shower. When Billy went out to play there was a big ______________ next to his sand box. He took his pail and an old spoon and began to play in the ______. Soon he was all ______________.

After a while he smelled the sweet scent of chocolate coming from the kitchen. Billy said to himself, "I bet Sue is making ______________."

Billy dropped his spoon and went to the back door to ask for some fudge. When Sue saw him she said, "You are too muddy to have anything to eat."

Billy answered, "Don't be such a ______________. All I need is to wash with some soap ______________ and water. Then may I have some fudge?" His sister said that when he was clean she would give him some fudge.

WORD LIST

Choose the missing word to complete each sentence.

mud	muddy	sudden
bud	fudge	fuddy-duddy
suds	puddle	

NAME ______________________________ DATE ______________

GETTING READY FOR THANKSGIVING

There was so much to do to get ready for Thanksgiving. Buffy needed a new dress. She and her mother went shopping. They got her a dress with ____________ on the collar and ruffles on the ____________ of each sleeve. Buffy saw some white fur ____________. They were so white and ____________. She asked if she could have one, but her mother said "No." At first she felt sad and became ____________. Then she decided there was no need to ____________. She should feel good because of her new dress.

Their next stop was the supermarket. They had to buy the turkey and the bread to make the ____________ to put in the turkey. They needed some bran to use in baking bran ____________.

The last stop was at the bakery. Buffy picked out a cream ________ for each member of her family for dessert. She knew this was going to be a very special holiday.

WORD LIST

Choose the missing word to complete each sentence.

puff	huffy	muffins
cuff	fluffy	stuffing
muffs	suffer	ruffles

NAME ______________________________ DATE ______________

DEBBIE'S MORNING

Debbie had given her mother a ______________ before she went out in the yard to play. She had played in the sand box and ______________ a big hole. Then she picked up an old board and found a big, strange ______________. "Ugh," she said to herself. "That is ______________." She put the board back and went into the garden. On a rose bush she found a small orange bug with dark spots. "What a pretty ______________ you are," she said. Just then her mother called her to come in.

"Wipe your feet so you don't get dirt on the ______________," her mother said. "I have to go to the ______________. Do you want to walk with me? You can put your doll in her ______________ and take her with us. Debbie ______________ up to her mother and said that she would like to do that. Then with Debbie ______________ her mother's hand, they went to get ready.

WORD LIST

Choose the missing word to complete each sentence.

hug	ugly	drugstore
dug	buggy	ladybug
bug	snuggled	
rugs	tugging	

NAME ______________________________ DATE ________________

THE END OF THE DAY

It had been a ______________ day. Mary was glad that it was over. When she was on her way to school a ______________ had teased her. He was a big ______________ of a boy. She was glad when a friendly ______________ passed them and the bully had gone on. Then in math she had to learn how to ______________. Adding and subtracting were not hard for her, but she found that multiplying was ______________.

On the way home she saw a ______________ flying over the bay. She wished she could be free to fly and not have to do ______________ work.

That night when she turned on her lamp to do her homework, she found that the ______________ had burned out. She got a new one and fixed the lamp.

Mary was upset. Everything seemed to have gone wrong that day.

After she got in bed she asked her mother if she would sing her a ______________. Somehow that helped her to feel better.

WORD LIST

Choose the missing word to complete each sentence.

full	hulk	multiply
dull	adult	lullaby
bulb	difficult	
bully	seagull	

NAME ______________________________ DATE ______________

A WALK IN THE RAIN

It was a rainy day in ______________. Scott held his ______________ over his head so he would not get wet. He was careful to ______________ over the puddles. He was hungry. His ______________ felt empty. He was chewing ______________ but that did not help. He began to think of the candy he liked best, red and yellow ______________. He wished for some ______________ pie like his mother made after Halloween. That was so ______________ to eat. He ran faster on the ______________ road. He was in a hurry to get home for dinner.

WORD LIST

Choose the missing word to complete each sentence.

gum	bumpy	pumpkin
jump	yummy	umbrella
tummy	summer	gumdrops

NAME ________________________ DATE ________________

RAIN AND SUN ON A SUNDAY

All ______________ morning the rain fell. Jim could hear the roar of ______________ far away. He had to stay at home ______________ the rain stopped falling and the ______________ came out.

He had just ______________ to eat his sandwich and drink his milk for ______________, when he looked out the window and saw the ______________. "What can I do for ______________ today?" he asked his mother.

"Why don't you ______________ over to Tim's house and see if he wants to play?" she said.

Jim ran along the side of the road. He saw old cars stacked up in a ______________ yard. He saw a black ______________ with a stripe on its back and a little ______________ rabbit with long ears. He left the road and crawled ______________ a fence to get to Tim's house. Jim and Tim played all afternoon, until the sun began to set. Then Jim went home.

WORD LIST

Choose the missing word to complete each sentence.

run	lunch	Sunday
sun	begun	thunder
fun	skunk	sunshine
under	until	
junk	bunny	

NAME ______________________________ DATE ________________

TOM'S AFTERNOON

After school Tom had to walk his ______________. They walked ______________ and down the block. They saw ______________ blooming in the yards. They saw a ______________ truck loaded with packages. Then they went ______________ to Tom's apartment. He went to his fish tank to feed his ______________. Then his mother called him to come eat ______________. He went right away because she became ______________ if he was late. After he ate supper his mother gave him a ______________ of milk and a ______________. She had not had time to make frosting, so she let him pour chocolate ______________ on the cupcake. Tom thought it was the best dessert he had ever eaten.

WORD LIST

Choose the missing word to complete each sentence.

up	pickup	cupcake
cup	supper	buttercups
upset	syrup	upstairs
guppy	puppy	

NAME ______________________ DATE ____________

AN AFTERNOON IN AUGUST

It was a hot ____________ afternoon. Bill was taking care of his baby brother. Since he was ten years old his mother had ____________ him to take care of Tommy when she went out. Bill could see that Tommy was tired and was getting ____________. He had been chewing on a ____________ of bread, but he tossed that away. He got up and walked over to the ____________ plant that had been put on the porch for the summer.

Bill said, "You know that you ____________ not play with that cactus. Do you want to get ____________ in trouble?"

Bill gave Tommy his toy ____________ to play with. It had been left out in the rain and had gotten ____________. One of its wheels had fallen off. Tommy did not want to play with it. Then Bill gave him the toy clown from his ____________ set. Just then a car went past on the ____________ road. Both boys watched until they could no longer see the car in the cloud of ____________. Soon their mother came home and they told her what they had done that day.

WORD LIST

Choose the missing word to complete each sentence.

us	rusty	trusted
bus	crust	fussy
dust	cactus	circus
must	dusty	August

NAME ______________________________ DATE ____________________

GETTING READY FOR SCHOOL

Ted washed his face and ______________ his teeth. He put his ______________ back in its holder. He looked out the window and saw that the snow that fell yesterday had turned to ______________. He was in no ______________ to get to school, but he knew it was time for breakfast. His mother was feeding his baby sister in the kitchen. The baby was fussing because she did not want to eat her ______________. His mother said, "I want you to ______________ now and eat your breakfast."

When his mother saw Ted she said, "Drink your orange juice. I will fix your egg with ______________ the way you like it." Ted finished breakfast. Then he started ______________ to get ready for school so he would not be late.

WORD LIST

Choose the missing word to complete each sentence.

hush	slush	mushrooms
mush	brushed	toothbrush
rush	rushing	

NAME ______________________________ DATE ______________

JAN HELPS HER MOTHER

Every Saturday morning Jan helps her mother. Last Saturday she made breakfast for her little brother, Jim. She fried an egg for him and put ______________ on his toast. Then she helped him put on his socks and shoes and ______________ his shirt. Then Jan and Jim cracked ________ for a pecan pie. Their mother asked Jan to take Jim to the barber shop for a ______________. When they came home it was time for lunch. Jan made two ______________ ______________ and jelly sandwiches. Jan ______________ each sandwich in two so it would be easy to eat. She was very careful when she was ______________ so she would not hurt herself.

After lunch her mother said, "I am glad to have your help, ________ you need time to play. Why don't you call your friends?" Jan and her friends went out to play jump rope, and soon the girls were having fun jumping double ______________.

WORD LIST

Choose the missing word to complete each sentence.

cut	Dutch	butter
but	button	haircut
nuts	cutting	peanut butter